AGS

The Solar System

Reading in the Content Area

by
William A. Kessman

AGS®

American Guidance Service, Inc.
4201 Woodland Road
Circle Pines, MN 55014-1796
1-800-328-2560

Photo credits:
cover—(digital composite of planets of the Solar System, digital starfield) Tony Stone Images; p.7—Photri; p. 8—Photri-Microstock; pp.14, 20, 26, 32—NASA; p. 37—Photri-Microstock; pp. 38, 44, 50, 55—NASA; p. 56—Tony Stone Images; pp. 62, 68, 73, 74, 80—NASA; p. 86—Photri-Microstock

Printed in the United States of America

ISBN 0-7854-2429-6

Order Number: 91575

A 0 9 8 7 6 5 4 3

Contents

Overview

For centuries, people have been trying to gather facts about the sky and beyond. People have always wondered about the mysteries of space.

In the 4th century B.C., Aristotle believed the sun revolved around the earth. People respected and believed his theories for centuries. Twenty centuries later, Copernicus put forth the theory that the earth revolved around the sun. He formed his theory based on naked-eye observations. His views were widely rejected. However, his thoughts made sense to some people and slowly, a scientific revolution began.

At the beginning of the 17th century A.D., Galileo built a telescope and began studying the skies more closely. He became very unpopular because he insisted that the earth revolved around the sun. Galileo studied the heavens with his telescope until he could explain his theories. However, the people of his time preferred to believe Aristotle's thoughts than Galileo's proofs. Even though his ideas were not accepted by the masses, some people could not reject the logic in what he was presenting.

Sir Isaac Newton was one of the people who took a serious look at Galileo's ideas. At the end of the 17th century, Newton was able to mathematically prove that Galileo was right. Unlike Galileo, Newton was not unpopular because of his beliefs. People did not reject his ideas. He became a popular hero. From Newton's time on, accepted fact has been that the earth and the other planets revolve around the sun. This book presents the known facts about the solar system and the rest of the universe. The tools and expeditions through which humans have learned about the universe create some stories that are truly out of this world.

As you read about the solar system, you will also learn how to get the most out of reading a textbook. Along with reading the text, you will complete some activities. These activities are explained below.

Setting the Stage
Setting the Stage is designed to help you get some quick ideas about the lesson you are going to read. You will quickly glance at the first two paragraphs and the last two paragraphs. Then, you will write a few words that give you a general idea what the lesson will be about.

Discussing the Background
Studies show that using information you already know can help you understand new information you read. To give you the best possible chance to understand what you are reading, you will be asked to discuss background information. After the first lesson, this information will come from the previous lesson. This method works well because it will help you build on information you learn as you read.

Words to Know
As you know, reading is difficult when you do not understand the words you are reading. Some of the most difficult words in this book are in bold letters in the text. These words are also listed in the Words to Know box. Although you will work with the vocabulary words after you read, you should read the words in the Words to Know box to become more familiar with them. As you read, if you come to a boldface word you do not know, you can look it up in the glossary.

Finding the Main Idea
Every reading selection has a main idea. Often, a group of paragraphs within an article or essay are related and have a main idea. You will be asked to highlight or circle the main idea in each paragraph. The main idea does not have to be complicated. It can be a single word, a phrase, a sentence, or more than one sentence.

When you are finished marking the main ideas, take a moment to read just the sentences and phrases you have marked. You will find you have a good overview of the lesson.

Making a Timeline
The purpose of the timeline is to see how different events relate to each other. You will be asked to place important dates from each lesson on a timeline. Sometimes, you will be asked to place dates from lessons you have already read on the timeline.

Using Context Clues
Context clues are one of the main ways readers have to figure out the meanings of unknown words. The words and sentences around an unknown word can give a lot of clues to the meaning of the word. Often, you will not learn exactly what the word means, but you will have a fairly good idea. In this exercise, you will be asked to give the meaning of a word and list a context clue for each word.

Reading for Details

Reading for Details teaches you to find details that support main ideas. You will be asked to fill in information in webs. These diagrams are a way to visually organize information.

Once you have written a main idea in a web, write three details to support the main idea. In many of the cases, there are more than three possible details. You can choose to only write three or to combine two or more of them in to one space.

These main idea/detail webs can be used to outline an entire article. This task could be completed by using a single web for each paragraph or by combining paragraphs on webs.

Making a Diagram

The final assignment in each lesson will ask you to make a drawing or diagram. Visually representing information you have learned can help you better understand it.

Getting the Main Idea

Unit 1

A view of Earth as seen by *Apollo 10* astronauts 100,000 miles away.

Every written selection, from paragraph to article, has a main idea. The main idea tells the selection's topic and what the selection says about that topic.

Often, the main idea of a selection will be the first or last sentence in the selection. This is called an *explicit* main idea, because the main idea is stated. Other selections may contain sentences that only hint about the main idea, or are *implicit*. Knowing a selection's main idea helps you to better understand what the selection says.

Two tools that will help you find the main idea are *context* and *details*. Context is the way words, sentences, and paragraphs work together to provide meaning. Details are bits of information that add to your understanding of a subject.

You will learn more about the main idea, context, and details in the next four lessons.

The Solar System

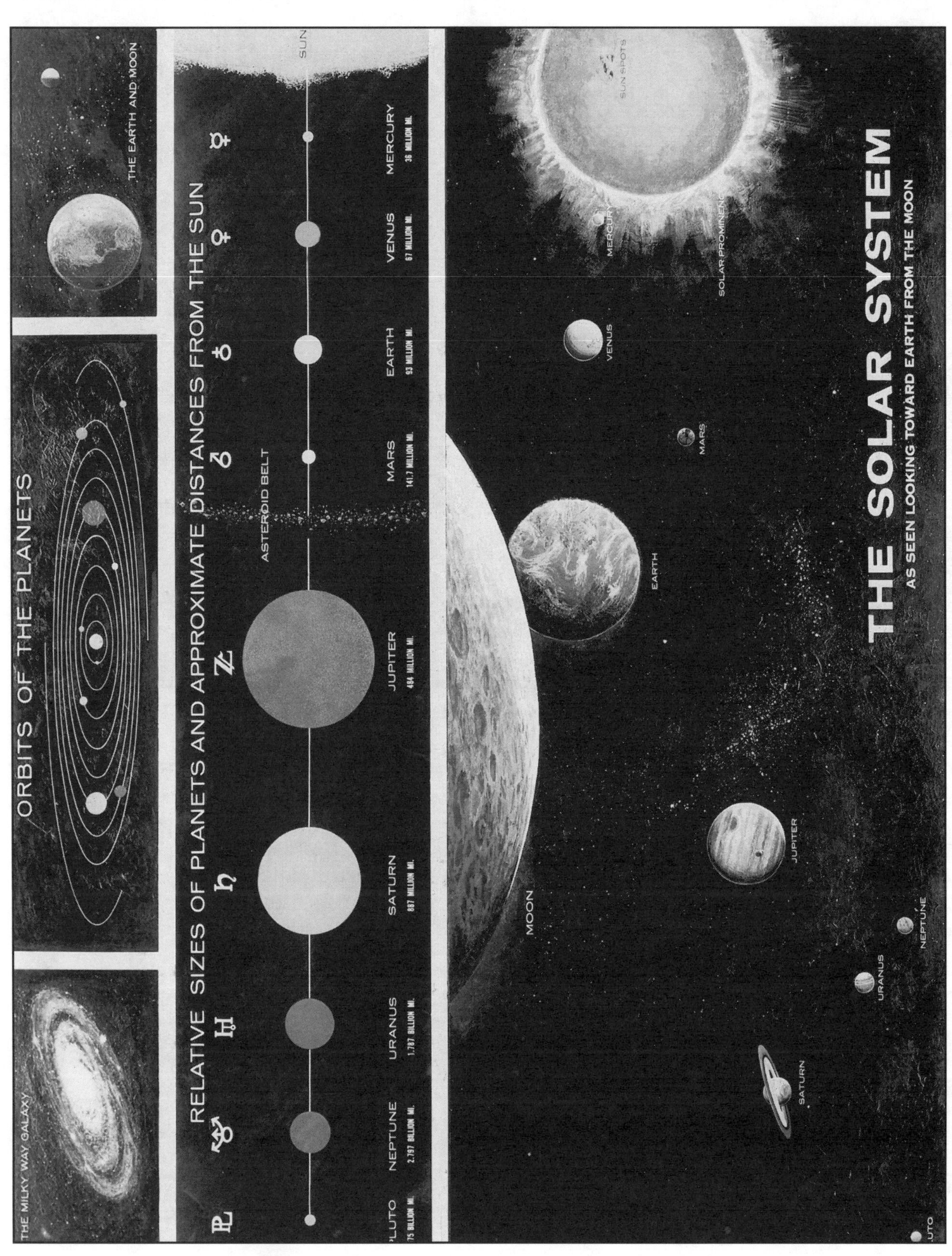

The sun and all the bodies that travel around it are called the solar system. This includes the sun, the nine planets, their moons, and billions of smaller objects called asteroids, meteoroids, and comets.

The Solar System

Lesson 1

A. Setting the Stage

Read the first two and last two paragraphs of this lesson. Write four nouns or phrases that appear to be key ideas.

1.	2.	3.	4.

B. Discussing the Background

As a group, answer and discuss these questions: What is Earth? What is the main source of energy used by people on Earth? If the sun disappeared, what would happen to Earth?

Words to Know
revolve
orbit
axis
matter
terrestrial
satellite
asteroid
meteoroid
comet
meteor
meteorite
crater
galaxy
astronomer

1 What is the solar system? The sun and all of the bodies that travel around it are called the solar system. The word *sol* means sun. The solar system could then be called the sun system. The sun is a star. It is also the center and most important part of the solar system.

2 Next in importance are the planets. Planets are objects that **revolve** in **orbit** around a star and are at least several thousand miles wide. There are nine planets which follow oval paths around the sun. As each planet travels around the sun, it spins on its **axis**. Even though an axis cannot be seen, it keeps the planet at the same angle. A planet's day equals the time it takes to spin around once on its axis. A planet's year is the amount of time needed to move once around the sun.

3 The planet nearest to the sun is Mercury. It is just 36 million miles away from the sun. Next in order are Venus, Earth, Mars, Jupiter, Saturn, Uranus, Neptune, and Pluto. The planet Earth is 93 million miles from the sun. Pluto, the farthest from the sun, is 3.67 billion miles away.

4 Planets were formed from **matter** such as water, ice, iron, rock, and gases. The four planets that are closest to the sun have lost most of their gases. These **terrestrial** planets are made mainly of iron and rock. The planets that are farthest from the sun still have much of their gases. They are Jupiter, Saturn, Uranus, and Neptune. They are called "gas giants." They are much larger than the other planets and are made mostly of hydrogen and helium. Pluto is the farthest planet, the smallest planet, and appears to be made of frozen gases.

The Solar System

The paths that planets follow around the sun are called orbits. Those planets closer to the sun have smaller orbits. They take less time to travel once around the sun. The earth needs 365 and 1/4 days (one year) to complete one orbit. Mercury, the closest planet to the sun, takes just 88 days. Far-away Pluto needs 248 Earth years to finish one orbit. **5**

Moons revolve around most planets. Moons are **satellites** and are smaller than most planets. There are more than 60 moons in the solar system. Some planets, like Jupiter and Saturn, have many satellites. The earth has only one satellite, the moon. **6**

Besides the planets and their moons, other bodies travel around the sun. They are called **asteroids, meteoroids**, and **comets.** **7**

Asteroids are planet-like chunks of rock. Most known asteroids travel around the sun between Mars and Jupiter. Some take other paths. About 40 asteroids cross inside Earth's orbit. Little chance exists of an asteroid crashing into Earth. **8**

Meteoroids are smaller pieces of rock and metal that fly around the sun. Scientists think they are pieces of comets and asteroids. Billions of them exist in the solar system. When they enter the earth's atmosphere, meteoroids are called shooting stars, or **meteors.** On certain nights, star watchers can see hundreds of meteors. This sight is called a meteor shower. The most famous meteor shower occurs each year around August 11. **9**

Every day, the orbiting Earth crosses the paths of some meteoroids. Most of these meteoroids are the size of a grain of sand. Some are the size of a golf ball, beach ball, or even a car. Meteors usually burn up completely before reaching Earth. A meteoroid that hits the earth is called a **meteorite.** Between five and 50 thousand years ago, scientists think a large meteorite landed in what is now Arizona. It left a crater nearly a mile across and about six hundred feet deep. Other parts of the world also have meteorite craters. **10**

Comets are miles-wide bodies of ice, metal, gas, and dust. They move around the sun in very long oval paths. As they near the sun, comets form "tails." These tails may stretch for millions of miles. When near the sun, comets shine brightly as they reflect the sun's light. **11**

Each comet takes a certain amount of time to travel around the sun. Halley's Comet is one of the brightest and most famous. It takes about 76 years to orbit the sun. It was last seen in 1986. The brightest comets take thousands or even millions of years to orbit the sun. There are about 1,500 known comets, with thousands more still to be discovered. **12**

13 As the planets, satellites, asteroids, meteoroids, and comets move in their orbits around the sun, the sun also revolves. It is part of a huge group of stars called a **galaxy.** Earth's galaxy is called the Milky Way. It has more than 100 billion stars.

14 All the stars that shine at night are really suns. Some of these suns have objects traveling around them, too. They might even have solar systems much like the sun and its planets. **Astronomers** do not know for sure because these stars are too far away.

15 From where did all the parts of the solar system come? Astronomers have been trying to answer this question for hundreds of years. Many astronomers think that the solar system began as a cloud of gases in space. They believe all parts of the solar system were formed from these gases at the same time. Other astronomers believe that the sun was formed first. The planets and other bodies came later from left-over gases. Scientists believe it is possible that many other stars also have a system of objects revolving around them. No one knows for sure. However, scientists continue to study these distant stars. Every year, more is learned about other stars.

C. Finding the Main Idea

Highlight or circle the main idea in each paragraph. Remember that the main idea of a paragraph is often the first or last sentence in that paragraph. Other times, the main idea has to be pieced together from more than one sentence.

D. Making a Timeline

Place the year that Halley's Comet last appeared and the year it will appear again on the timeline. Write a label for each date.

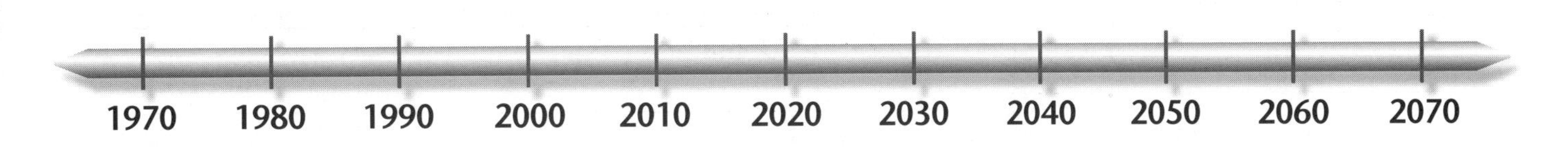

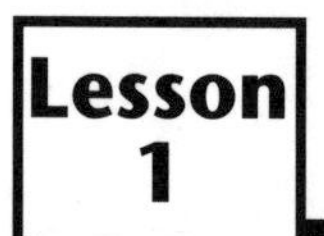

E. Using Context Clues

Find the following four vocabulary words in the article. The words and sentences around each word give a clue to its meaning. Use these clues to write a meaning for each word. For each vocabulary word, describe one clue that you used.

1. revolve

Meaning: ______________________

____

____

Clue: ______________________

____

2. axis

Meaning: ______________________

____

____

Clue: ______________________

____

3. terrestrial

Meaning: ______________________

____

____

Clue: ______________________

____

4. satellites

Meaning: ______________________

____

____

Clue: ______________________

____

F. Reading for Details

Reread the two paragraphs identified below. Then, complete the main idea/detail webs.

Paragraph # 2

Main Idea: ______________________

____

____

Supporting Detail #1

Supporting Detail #2

Supporting Detail #3

Paragraph # 10

Main Idea: ______________________

____

____

Supporting Detail #1

Supporting Detail #2

Supporting Detail #3

G. Giving Short Answers

Use complete sentences to answer each of the questions below.

1. What is the difference between a meteor, a meteoroid, and a meteorite?

____

____

2. How do scientists know which objects are in the solar system and which are not?

____

____

3. Why is the sun considered the most important part of the solar system?

____

____

H. Making a Diagram

Draw a picture showing the ten main parts of the solar system. Show them in position in relation to each other.

Lesson 2

Stars

Nebulas are huge clouds of dust and gas from which stars are formed. The "Horsehead" Nebula is shown here.

Stars

Lesson 2

A. Setting the Stage

Read the first two and last two paragraphs of this lesson. Write four nouns or phrases that appear to be key ideas.

1.	2.	3.	4.

B. Discussing the Background

Reread the last two paragraphs of Lesson 1. As a group, discuss the relationship between Lesson 1 and Lesson 2.

Words to Know

- black dwarf
- gravity
- nova
- supernova
- nebula
- constellation
- star cluster
- universe
- telescope
- light-year

1 On a clear night you can see many stars in the sky. Sometimes you can count hundreds of them. Stars look like twinkling jewels in the night sky. Yet, they don't really twinkle at all. Stars seem to twinkle because the air around them is always moving. The moving air distorts the view.

2 What is a star? How are stars formed? A star is a huge, hot glowing globe of gas. This globe gives off large amounts of energy. Scientists think that stars are formed from thick clouds of dust and gas whirling around in space. After stars are formed, they go through different stages. They end their lives as dark, cold objects called **black dwarfs.**

3 Most stars are huge compared to planets. The nearest star, the sun, is a medium-sized star. Even though the sun is medium-sized, thousands of Earths could fit inside. It is only one of billions of stars. The other stars are all very far away. The distance makes them all seem smaller than the sun. Of the far away stars, many seem much larger and brighter than the others. They appear that way because they are closer to Earth. Stars have a strong force of **gravity.** This force pulls objects towards stars.

4 There are many different stars in the galaxy. Some are yellow, like the sun. Others, like Sirius, are hotter and look blue or white. Cooler stars are much redder and sometimes quite huge. Antares, for example, is a red, supergiant star. If Antares were to change places with the sun, it would stretch beyond Earth. It would fill the orbit of Mars as well.

Stars

Stars have many different levels of brightness. Some stars look like they are single points of light. Yet, they are really two or more stars very near to each other. The bright star, Algol, is an example. Algol has a twin star. This star passes in front of Algol every two days. So, the brightness of Algol changes often. Other stars show changes in brightness as they change in size. Mira is an example of this kind of star. **5**

Sometimes a star will suddenly shine very brightly for a short time. Then, it fades in a few months or years. This change is caused by powerful explosions on the surface of the star. These explosions blow away part of the star. This kind of star is called a **nova.** **6**

A star hardly ever explodes completely. If it does, the star becomes even brighter than a nova and is called a **supernova.** One such supernova was seen by the Chinese in the year 1054. The remains of this explosion can still be seen in the sky. They are part of the Crab Nebula. A **nebula** is a great cloud of dust and gas from which stars are formed. **7**

Stars are always moving quickly through space. Even so, they seem to stay in the same patterns. This is true because stars are so far away. The patterns that stars make are called **constellations.** Long ago, astronomers named these constellations after animals, mythical gods, and heroes. One example is Ursa Major (the Great Bear). Star watchers can see it in the northern skies throughout the year. **8**

Usually, the stars in a constellation are not grouped together. Yet, when seen from Earth, these stars seem to lie in the same direction. There are some groups of stars that seem to be huddled together in the sky. Some of these **star clusters** are within the Milky Way Galaxy. A well-known example of such a cluster is the Pleiades, or "Seven Sisters." **9**

Astronomers have been studying the stars in the **universe** for hundreds of years. To do this, they now use powerful **telescopes.** Using this method, astronomers have discovered a number of galaxies other than the Milky Way. The nearest large galaxy is called the Andromeda galaxy. It is two million **light-years** away. That means light given off from the Andromeda Galaxy is seen on Earth two million years after it was given off. Other galaxies in the universe are more than a thousand times farther away than Andromeda. No one knows what might lie beyond them. **10**

Stars

Lesson 2

11 The sun is 93 million miles from Earth. Compared to the other stars, 93 million miles is close. Imagine if a spacecraft could travel 100 miles per second. At this speed, the craft would reach the nearest star in 13,333 years. Today's technology can not create spacecraft that can travel this fast. Even if people could travel at this speed, the trip could not be made within a person's lifetime. For these reasons, humans are not likely to travel to stars in this century.

12 Even a spacecraft without passengers cannot travel to another star. Engines made with current technology need to be cooled. Using today's knowledge, people cannot build an engine that can travel to the stars and cool itself. Therefore, humans are unable to send a spacecraft to visit stars any time soon.

13 The closest today's people will come to visiting the stars is through telescopes. Astronomers have charted and named many stars. In 1994, the Hubble Space Telescope shot a first-time picture of Gliese. This star is ten times smaller than the sun. In 1997, Hubble sighted the brightest known star. The star is ten million times more powerful than the sun. In six seconds, this powerful star gives off as much energy as the sun gives off in one year. Using the Hubble Space Telescope, scientists study all stars they can see—big and small.

14 Astronomers are interested in the many stars in the sky. However, the sun is the most important star for people on Earth to understand. The sun is the center of the solar system and the root of all life on Earth.

C. Finding the Main Idea

Highlight or circle the main idea in each paragraph. Remember that the main idea of a paragraph is often the first or last sentence in that paragraph. Other times, the main idea has to be pieced together from more than one sentence.

D. Making a Timeline

Place two dates the Hubble Space Telescope made new discoveries on the timeline. Write two or three words to identify the importance of each date.

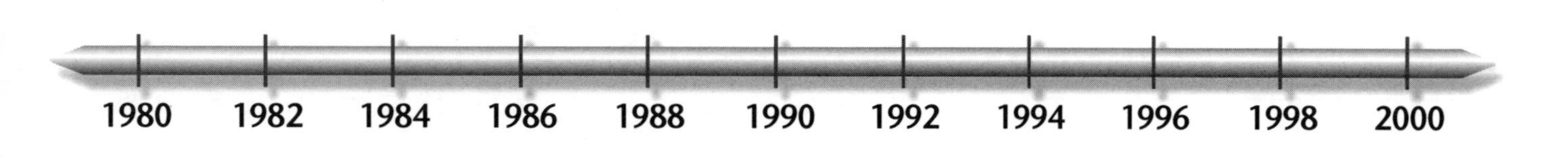

E. Using Context Clues

Find the following four vocabulary words in the article. The words and sentences around each word give a clue to its meaning. Use these clues to write a meaning for each word. For each vocabulary word, describe one clue that you used.

1. gravity

Meaning: ______________________

____

____

Clue: ______________________

____

2. supernova

Meaning: ______________________

____

____

Clue: ______________________

____

3. universe

Meaning: ______________________

____

____

Clue: ______________________

____

4. telescopes

Meaning: ______________________

____

____

Clue: ______________________

____

F. Reading for Details

Reread the two paragraphs identified below. Then, complete the main idea/detail webs.

Paragraph # 3

Main Idea: ______________________

____

____

Supporting Detail #1

Supporting Detail #2

Supporting Detail #3

Paragraph # 9

Main Idea: ______________________

____

____

Supporting Detail #1

Supporting Detail #2

Supporting Detail #3

G. Giving Short Answers

Use complete sentences to answer each of the questions below.

1. Do stars really twinkle? Why not?

2. How do scientists think stars are formed?

3. Why do stars seem to stay in the same patterns?

H. Making a Diagram

Draw two constellations. One should be an actual constellation. (You may need to find information in a reference book for this drawing.) The other should be a created constellation. Add the connecting lines between the stars. Write the names for both constellations.

The Sun

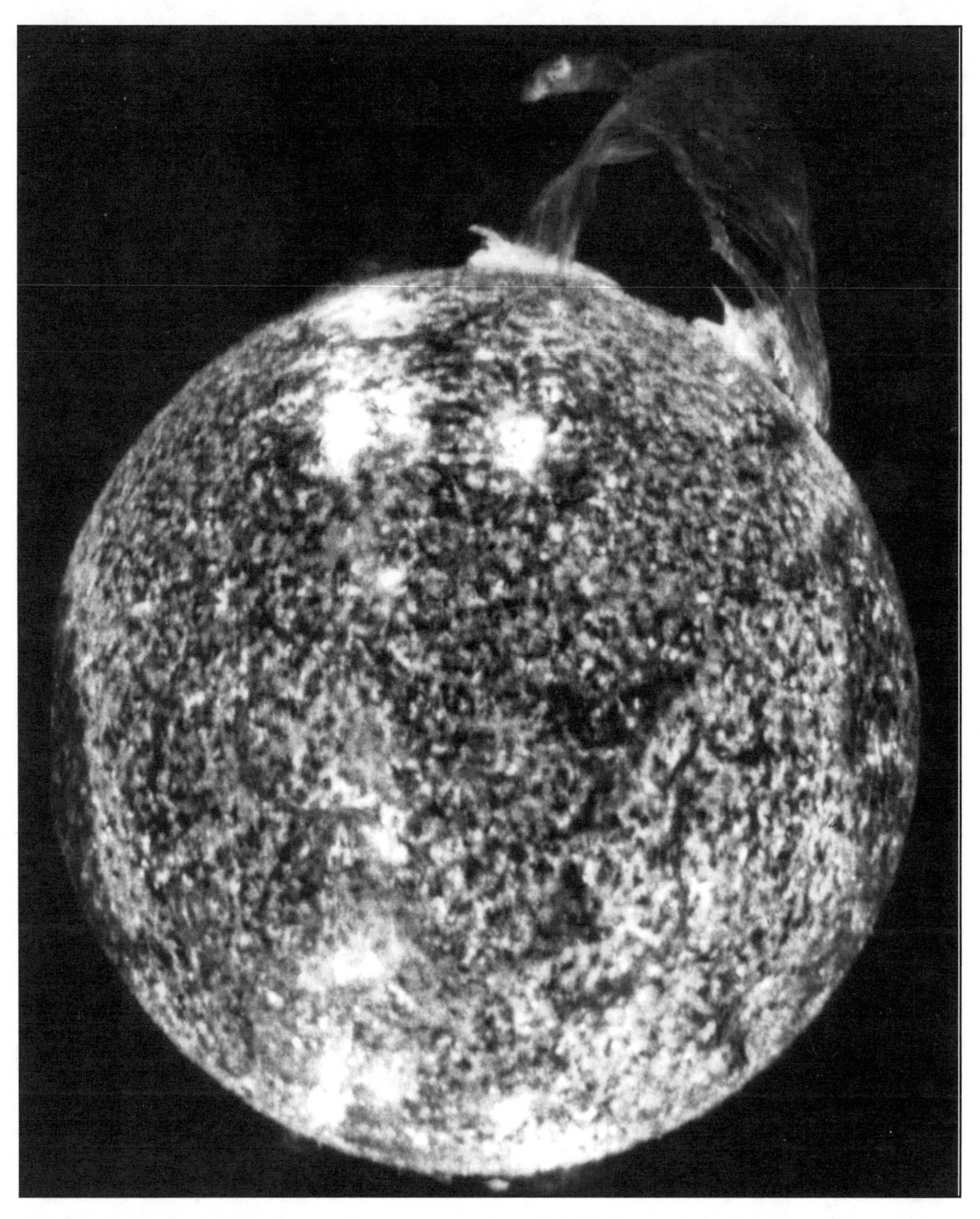

This photograph of the sun was taken on December 19, 1973, by NASA's *Skylab 4*. It shows one of the most spectacular solar flares ever recorded. The flare spans almost 400,000 miles across the solar surface and looks like a twisted sheet of gas unwinding itself.

The Sun

Lesson 3

A. Setting the Stage

Read the first two and last two paragraphs of this lesson. Write four nouns or phrases that appear to be key ideas.			
1.	**2.**	**3.**	**4.**

B. Discussing the Background

Reread the last two paragraphs of Lesson 2. As a group, discuss the relationship between Lesson 2 and Lesson 3.

Words to Know
mass
core
emit
photosphere
chromosphere
solar flare
particle
corona

1 The sun is the biggest and most important object in the solar system. This statement is now a known fact. However, for centuries, people argued about the sun's position.

2 For many centuries, Earth was accepted as the center of the solar system. People rejected the idea that the sun was the center of the solar system. They wanted Earth to be the most important part of the solar system. Even many scientists believed the sun and the other planets revolved around the earth. They ignored facts put out to prove otherwise. Finally, at the end of the 18th century, Isaac Newton convinced people to accept that the sun was the center of the solar system.

3 Stars are much bigger than planets. Still, astronomers believe that stars were formed in the same way as planets. Pieces of matter clung together and gathered other pieces. Slowly, the mass grew larger. A very large, burning **mass** is a star. The solar system has only one star, the sun. It is the largest mass in the solar system. Because it is such a large mass, the sun has a strong force of gravity. This force pulls at the planets. The planets are large enough to pull back. Since they can pull back, the planets are not sucked into the sun.

4 Orbits are the result of the sun and planets pulling on each other. If the planets were larger or stronger, they would move away from the sun into outer space. Other smaller objects in the solar system also revolve around the sun. These items are either large enough to hold themselves in orbit or are locked into a planet's orbit.

Lesson 3

The Sun

The sun is a medium-sized star and the earth is a medium-sized planet. However, the sun looks huge compared to the earth. Think of the sun as being the size of a basketball. The largest planet would then be no bigger than a golf ball. The smallest would be smaller than a pencil dot. More than a million Earth's could fit within the sun. The sun does not look big from Earth because it is 93 million miles away. **5**

The sun is hotter than anything on Earth. The sun is much hotter than fire. When an object gets very hot, it turns into gases. Most of the sun is a gas called hydrogen. The temperature of the sun's surface is about 5,527 degrees Celsius (9,980 degrees Fahrenheit). The temperature at the sun's **core** is even hotter at about 15 million °C (27 million °F). **6**

7

The sun gives off energy. The earth gets all of its energy from the sun. This energy keeps things on Earth alive. Life grows and fuel is formed because the sun shines upon the earth.

Deep inside the sun, large amounts of heat, light, and other forms of energy are **emitted.** This energy rises to the sun's surface and is sent out in rays in all directions. Only a very small amount of that energy reaches the earth. Sometimes, even this small amount is too much. People who sunburn easily would happily turn the sun down a little! **8**

Life on Earth would not exist without the sun. The earth would always be darker than night. Life needs light energy from the sun to survive. Also, without the sun, every day on Earth would be cold. The days would be colder than the coldest day at the north pole. Neither animals nor plants would survive the extreme cold temperatures. If the sun were to disappear, life on Earth as as it is now would be impossible. **9**

The sun is also vital to the other planets in the solar system. The sun helps hold the planets in their orbits and supports any life that might exist. However, no proof exists that shows life on other planets in the Milky Way. The other planets all appear to be too hot or too cold. **10**

The sun's surface is not solid. It is a boiling mass of hot gases, called the **photosphere.** Photosphere means light sphere. At times, dark marks appear on the sun's surface. These spots are called sunspots. These sunspots are much cooler than the photosphere around them. Sunspots move from east to west around the sun. Some last for months, while others fade in a matter of hours. **11**

The Sun

Lesson 3

12 Gases surround the sun just above its surface. This area of gases is called the sun's atmosphere. The lower part of the sun's atmosphere is called the **chromosphere** (meaning "color sphere"). This lower atmosphere stretches outward for several thousand miles. **Solar flares** often happen in the chromosphere. Scientists think that these powerful explosions are set off by sunspots. Solar flares give off energy in the form of waves and **particles.** These waves and particles of energy spread out into space far beyond the earth. These flares even interfere with radio air waves.

13 The upper part of the sun's atmosphere is called the **corona,** which means crown. It can be divided into two layers. The lower layer is called the K-corona. It is made of thin gases and billions of very tiny particles of matter. The upper layer is called the F-corona. It stretches for millions of miles into space.

14 NASA's spacecraft have increased scientists' understanding of the sun. In 1973, NASA's *Skylab* captured a spectacular solar flare image. In 1996, a spacecraft took a picture of the sun's corona. This image provided more details than ever before.

15 The sun and the whole solar system cover a very large area. The distance from one end to the other is 3.6 billion miles. As large as this sounds, it is still only a tiny part of the Milky Way.

C. Finding the Main Idea

Highlight or circle the main idea in each paragraph. Remember that the main idea of a paragraph is often the first or last sentence in that paragraph. Other times, the main idea has to be pieced together from more than one sentence.

D. Making a Timeline

Place two dates that new images of the sun were taken on the timeline. Write two or three words to identify the importance of each date.

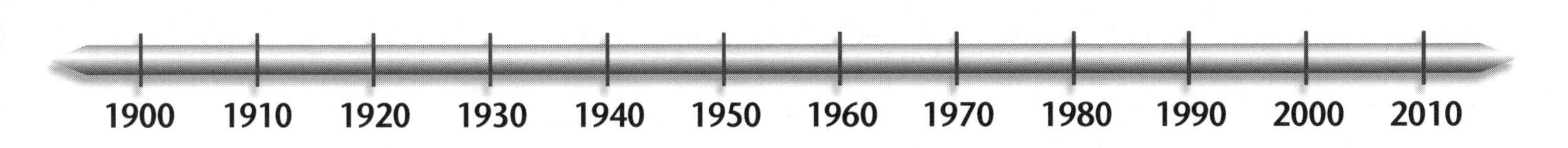

E. Using Context Clues

Find the following four vocabulary words in the article. The words and sentences around each word give a clue to its meaning. Use these clues to write a meaning for each word. For each vocabulary word, describe one clue that you used.

1. mass

Meaning: ______________________

____

____

Clue: ______________________

____

2. photosphere

Meaning: ______________________

____

____

Clue: ______________________

____

3. core

Meaning: ______________________

____

____

Clue: ______________________

____

4. emitted

Meaning: ______________________

____

____

Clue: ______________________

____

F. Reading for Details

Reread the two paragraphs identified below. Then, complete the main idea/detail webs.

Paragraph # 2

Main Idea: ______________________

____

____

Supporting Detail #1

Supporting Detail #2

Supporting Detail #3

Paragraph # 14

Main Idea: ______________________

____

____

Supporting Detail #1

Supporting Detail #2

Supporting Detail #3

The Sun

G. Giving Short Answers

Use complete sentences to answer each of the questions below.

1. How big is the solar system compared to the entire Milky Way?

____

____

2. Why do the planets stay in their orbits around the sun?

____

____

3. Some people believe that Earth is the only planet with life because it is the one planet that is the perfect distance from the sun. Explain this reasoning.

____

____

H. Making a Diagram

Draw the sun showing its layers. Label the photosphere, atmosphere, chromosphere, corona, K-corona, and F-corona.

The Milky Way

The Milky Way's stars fan out from the middle in wide, curving arms like a pinwheel. Our solar system is out in one of the arms. Earth is about 27,000-28,000 light-years away from the Milky Way's center.

The Milky Way

Lesson 4

A. Setting the Stage

Read the first two and last two paragraphs of this lesson. Write four nouns or phrases that appear to be key ideas.

1.	2.	3.	4.

B. Discussing the Background

Reread the last two paragraphs of Lesson 3. As a group, discuss the relationship between Lesson 3 and Lesson 4.

Words to Know
fluke
evolve
interstellar
alter
spiral

1 The Milky Way is one of billions of galaxies in the universe. A galaxy is a huge system of stars. These stars are closer to each other than they are to stars in other galaxies. The solar system is a tiny part of the Milky Way Galaxy. The sun and its orbiting planets are about 30,000 light-years from the center of the Milky Way. People cannot travel as fast as the speed of light. Therefore, the center of the Milky Way is too far away for people on Earth to visit. The whole galaxy spins slowly in space. The solar system travels around the center of the Milky Way once every 225 million years.

2 Many stars in the Milky Way have their own solar systems. Some astronomers believe that many of these solar systems may have some form of life. The closest solar system that might have animal and plant life is about 100 light-years away. A radio message sent to this solar system at the speed of light would arrive in 100 years!

3 Since other solar systems are so far away, scientists know little about them. A **fluke** might give people a chance to learn about another solar system. The fluke is comet P/Wild 2. The comet is new to the solar system and has recently gotten close enough to Earth to be studied. Scientists hope to learn something about the solar system from which P/Wild2 has come. With luck, the comet will provide information about Earth's solar system. One of the most interesting mysteries is how a group of masses **evolved** into the sun and its planets.

Comet P/Wild 2 has not been overheated nor degassed by the sun. P/Wild 2 provides a rare chance to learn about objects that exist between the stars. When the comet first came into the solar system, it orbited between Jupiter and Uranus. This location was far away and made studying the **interstellar** matter difficult. On September 10, 1974, the comet's orbit was **altered** when Jupiter passed close by. The comet now orbits between Mars and Jupiter, which is much closer to Earth. On February 7, 1999, a spacecraft launched and headed towards P/Wild2. From February through mid-2004, the spacecraft will collect interstellar dust. Perhaps scientists will learn something about other parts of the Milky Way. The spacecraft's return to Earth is planned for 2006. **4**

Galaxies have many different shapes. Some are shaped like a flattened ball. Others look like round fuzzy balls. The Milky Way is shaped like a pancake with a bulge in the middle. People can see the Milky Way on a dark, clear, summer night. On these nights, the galaxy looks like a wide, fuzzy band across the sky. It only looks this way from the inside. From the outside, the Milky Way looks like a huge pinwheel. Its stars fan out from the middle in wide, curving arms. These arms give the Milky Way a **spiral** shape. The solar system is out in one of the spiral arms. **5**

The Milky Way is huge. Next to it, the solar system is but a tiny speck. A spaceship cannot travel from one end of the Milky Way to the other. At the speed of light, this trip would take 100,000 years. Today's spaceships cannot go nearly that fast so the trip would take much longer. **6**

The Milky Way contains billions of stars. Many stars in the Milky Way are grouped in clusters. Clusters in the spiral arms contain up to 1,000 stars. These stars are young. Outside the arms are larger clusters with up to a million stars. These stars are some of the oldest in Earth's galaxy. **7**

The stars in the Milky Way Galaxy are far apart from each other. However, the space between the stars is not empty. Huge clouds of dust and gas exist there. These clouds are called nebulas. Here, new stars are formed. Often, a nebula has stars inside it and glows brightly. The Orion Nebula is an example. **8**

The Milky Way has many dark spaces. They are formed by nebulas. These nebulas do not glow. They are dark and hide the stars behind them. Most of the stars in the center of the Milky Way are hidden by many dark nebulas. Therefore, neither the center of the galaxy nor its spiral arms can be seen from Earth. **9**

The Milky Way

Lesson 4

10 For a long time, astronomers believed the Milky Way to be the only galaxy in the universe. They thought the different spirals and shining objects they saw through telescopes were nebulas. In the 1920s, astronomer Edwin Hubble took pictures of these nebulas. He used the largest telescope made at that time. Hubble showed that these spirals and shiny objects were not nebulas at all. They were really galaxies far beyond the Milky Way. Scientists now know that there are billions of galaxies in space.

11 Today, the Hubble Space Telescope (named after Edwin Hubble, not created by him) is collecting a great amount of data. This tool will likely unlock many secrets about the Milky Way. Already, the telescope has discovered new stars, new mysteries, and new facts about the planets in the solar system. The Hubble also collects information about Earth's natural satellite, the moon.

C. Finding the Main Idea

Highlight or circle the main idea in each paragraph. Remember that the main idea of a paragraph is often the first or last sentence in that paragraph. Other times, the main idea has to be pieced together from more than one sentence.

D. Making a Timeline

Place two important dates from this lesson on the timeline. Write two or three words to identify the importance of each date.

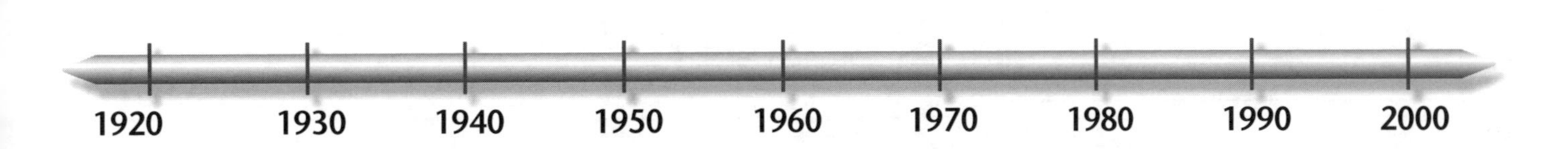

E. Using Context Clues

Find the following four vocabulary words in the article. The words and sentences around each word give a clue to its meaning. Use these clues to write a meaning for each word. For each vocabulary word, describe one clue that you need.

1. fluke

Meaning: ______________________________

____

____

Clue: ______________________________

____

2. interstellar

Meaning: ______________________________

____

____

Clue: ______________________________

____

3. altered

Meaning: ______________________________

____

____

Clue: ______________________________

____

4. spiral

Meaning: ______________________________

____

____

Clue: ______________________________

____

F. Reading for Details

Reread the two paragraphs identified below. Then, complete the main idea/detail webs.

Paragraph # 4

Main Idea: ______________________________

____

____

Supporting Detail #1

Supporting Detail #2

Supporting Detail #3

Paragraph # 11

Main Idea: ______________________________

____

____

Supporting Detail #1

Supporting Detail #2

Supporting Detail #3

The Milky Way

Lesson 4

G. Giving Short Answers

Use complete sentences to answer each of the questions below.

1. Why don't scientists know much about other solar systems?

____

____

2. Explain the relationship between planets, the solar system, the Milky Way, and the universe.

____

____

3. Why is the chance to learn from the P/Wild 2 comet a fluke?

____

____

H. Making a Diagram

Draw a picture of the Milky Way. Label a possible location for the solar system.

Earth's Moon

This photo shows the moon's far side, as taken by the *Apollo 17* crew in December of 1972.

Earth's Moon

Lesson 5

A. Setting the Stage

Read the first two and last two paragraphs of this lesson. Write four nouns or phrases that appear to be key ideas.			
1.	2.	3.	4.

B. Discussing the Background

Reread the last two paragraphs of Lesson 4. As a group, discuss the relationship between Lesson 4 and Lesson 5.

Words to Know
phase
astronaut
lunar
data
clash
plain
terrain
rilles
volcano

1 The moon is Earth's only natural satellite. Remember, an object that revolves around a planet is called a satellite or moon. A satellite is much smaller than the planet it orbits.

2 The moon is much smaller than Earth. Forty-nine moons are needed to fill the space taken up by Earth. The moon is also much lighter than Earth. It would take 81 moons to equal Earth's weight. The moon's gravity is much weaker than Earth's, too. A person who weighs 100 pounds on Earth would weigh only 17 pounds on the moon because there is much less gravity acting upon the person.

3 Earth's gravity tugs at the moon and keeps the moon from zooming off into space. The moon orbits Earth once about every 27 days. It takes this same amount of time for the moon to turn once on its axis. Therefore, the same side of the moon always faces Earth. The side of the moon that we never see is sometimes called the far side. People can see the moon by the sunlight it reflects. As the moon travels around Earth, people see different amounts of the lighted side. These amounts form the bright shapes seen from Earth. Scientists call these shapes the **phases** of the moon.

Earth's Moon

The moon is the only other body in the solar system on which humans have walked. NASA **astronauts** Neil Armstrong and Buzz Aldrin were the first humans to land on the moon. They left a plaque that reads "Here men from the planet Earth first set foot upon the moon in July, 1969, A.D. We came in peace for all mankind." The message was from all the people on Earth, not just from the United States. This choice was part of America's goal to make space travel an international concern. **4**

Since 1969, ten other United States astronauts have been to the moon. Astronauts used a vehicle called the **Lunar** Rover to get around the moon. In 1994, spacecraft Clementine made many maps of the moon. In 1998, Lunar Prospector was launched. Its mission was also to make moon maps. These trips have helped scientists gather useful **data.** Scientists now know more about the moon than ever before. **5**

6 Looking at the moon from Earth, sky watchers see light and dark patches on the moon's surface. Long ago, astronomers thought that the dark patches of the moon were seas. On the moon missions, astronauts discovered that these seas are really huge, dry **plains.** The light patches on the moon's surface are mountains. These mountains were formed from rock. Some of this moon rock is about 4.6 billion years old. Scientists have studied the moon rock brought back to Earth. Many scientists now believe the moon was created when Earth crashed into a large body. After the impact, the earth's gravity captured a broken piece of matter. This broken matter, the moon, began to orbit the earth.

Gravity **clashes** between the earth and the moon can be seen daily. The most common examples of these clashes are the tides. The moon's gravity pulls stronger on the side of the earth nearest to the moon. The earth rotates faster than the moon. This causes the bulges to move around the earth making two high tides per day. **7**

The moon's **terrain** is made up of dust and rock. It has ridges and deep cracks called **rilles.** Millions of craters of all sizes cover the ground. Some are very small. Others are huge. The smallest are less than one foot wide. Others are miles wide. One of the largest of the moon's craters is called Clavius. It is 12,000 feet deep and 140 miles wide. Some of the moon's craters were formed by **volcanoes.** Most of them were formed about 4 billion years ago by asteroids or meteorites crashing into the moon. **8**

The moon has no weather. There is no air or water. However, the Clementine mission made a new discovery. Ice appears to exist on the south pole of the moon. The Lunar Prospector mission repeated this finding. Lunar Prospector also sensed ice on the moon's north pole. **9**

Earth's Moon

At the end of Lunar Prospector's mission, NASA crashed the spacecraft into the moon's south pole. NASA hoped the crash would stir up water molecules that would prove the presence of ice. The plan did not give the desired results. NASA knew the chances of success were only about ten percent. Scientists also knew that only a positive finding would be meaningful. So, not finding a sign of ice does not mean there is no ice on the moon. **10**

The moon has no clouds, rain, snow, or wind. Plants do not grow there. Animals do not live there. Nothing has been found on the moon that shows that life ever existed there. As the ice at the poles is studied, this fact could change. **11**

Astronauts have shown that people can live on the moon. Air, water, and food would have to be taken from Earth. People would wear spacesuits to control temperature and air pressure. The moon's temperature during the day rises to 260°F. At night, it drops to –250°F. This range would not work for humans without climate control. **12**

C. Finding the Main Idea

Highlight or circle the main idea in each paragraph. Remember that the main idea of a paragraph is often the first or last sentence in that paragraph. Other times, the main idea has to be pieced together from more than one sentence.

D. Making a Timeline

Place two important dates from this lesson on the timeline. Write two or three words to identify the importance of each date.

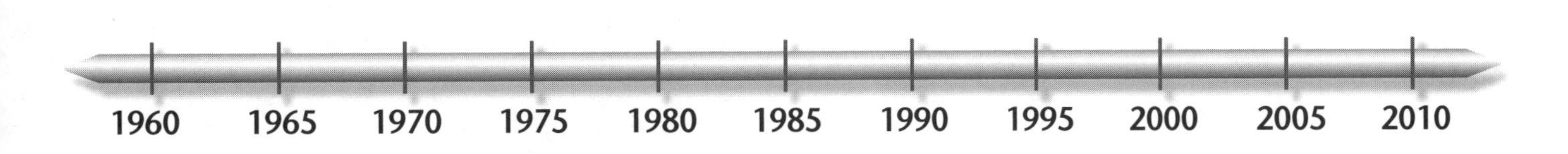

E. Reading for Details

Reread the two paragraphs identified below. Then, complete the main idea/detail webs.

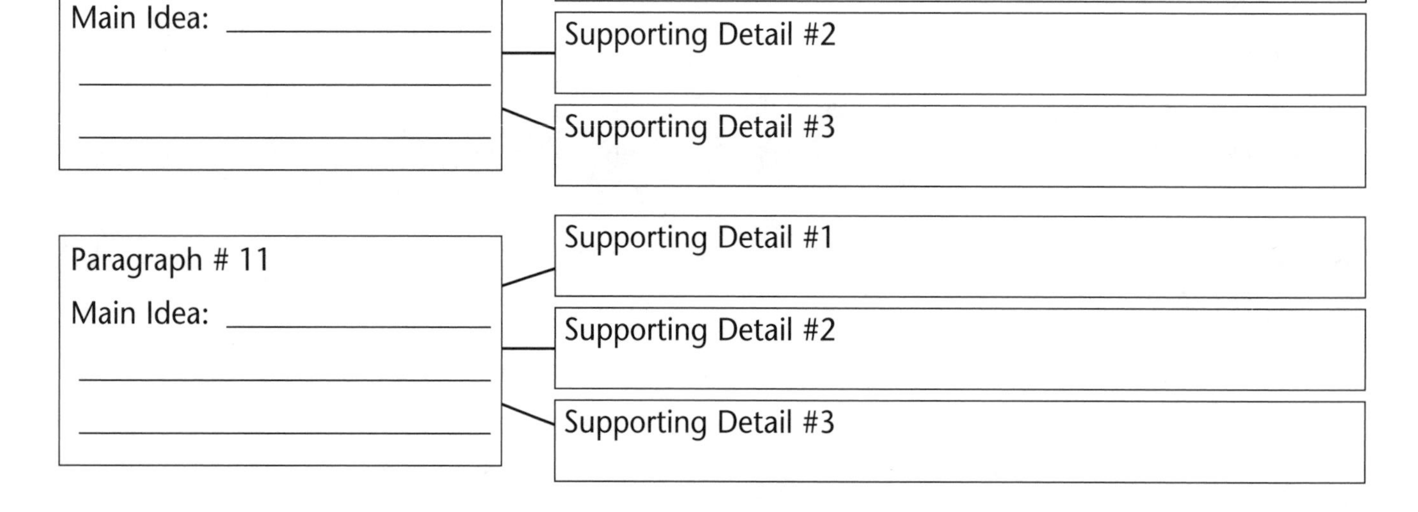

F. Making a Diagram

Draw the moon and include features of its terrain: rocks, rilles, craters, and plains. Label these features.

Reading for Details

Unit 2

This image shows the planets of the solar system as seen from the surface of the moon. A solar eclipse can be seen above and behind Earth.

Details are sometimes called facts. They are small bits of information. Details explain or tell about the main idea of a paragraph or reading selection. Reading for details means finding and getting the facts and ideas that help to make the main point.

You can find the details in a paragraph or reading selection by asking yourself questions.

If you ask yourself *who,* your answer will be a detail about a person.

If you ask yourself *what,* your answer will be a detail about a thing.

If you ask *when,* your answer will be a detail about time.

If you ask *where,* your answer will be a detail about a place.

Details, then, answer such questions as *Who? What? When? Where? Why? How? How many? How much? Which one?*

Paying attention to details helps you better understand what you are reading.

Mercury

Mercury's cratered surface can be seen in this image from the Mariner 10 spacecraft.

Mercury

Lesson 6

A. Setting the Stage

Read the first two and last two paragraphs of this lesson. Write four nouns or phrases that appear to be key ideas.

1.	2.	3.	4.

B. Discussing the Background

Reread the last two paragraphs of Lesson 5. As a group, discuss the relationship between Lesson 5 and Lesson 6.

Words to Know
unaided
twilight
lava
scarp
radar

1 Mercury is the closest planet to the sun. It is only 36 million miles away.

2 One might say that it is a sunbaked planet. During the day, Mercury gets very hot. The temperature can go as high as 427°C (800°F). At night, Mercury becomes very, very cold. The temperature can go as low as –184°C (–300°F). No other planet in the solar system has such huge changes in temperature.

3 Mercury is the fastest of all the planets. It speeds around the sun in only 88 days. Because it travels so fast, Mercury was named after the speedy Roman messenger of the gods. Yet, Mercury turns very slowly on its axis. A day on Mercury is as long as 59 days on Earth. The very long day is one of the reasons the planet gets so hot. Likewise, the very long night is one of the reasons the planet gets so cold.

4 Mercury is also a small planet. It is less than half the size of Earth. Pluto is the only planet smaller than Mercury. Because of Mercury's small size, its gravity is much weaker than Earth's. A person who weighs 100 pounds on Earth would weigh only 38 pounds on Mercury.

5 People can often see Mercury with the **unaided** eye in the evening. It is amazing that people can see something so far away without a telescope. However, the planet is close to the sun and is difficult to find in the **twilight** sky.

6 The first good look at Mercury came from the Mariner 10 spacecraft. Mariner 10 flew past Mercury three times during the 1970s. It took more than 3,000 pictures of Mercury and sent them back to Earth. Mariner 10 was called MVM. This is short for Mariner Venus Mercury. It was given this name because it visited both Venus and Mercury.

7 The pictures sent back by Mariner 10 showed that Mercury's surface is like the moon's. It is covered with dust and craters of all sizes. The largest of Mercury's craters is 800 miles across. It is called the Caloris Basin. Scientists believe that a meteoroid formed this large crater when it crashed into the planet's surface. The force of the meteoroid's crash also pushed up huge mountains around the edges of the crater. Flying bits of rock cut out long valleys on Mercury's surface.

8 Some of the craters on Mercury are filled with **lava.** Scientists think that the lava may have come from volcanoes. Volcanoes spill lava when liquid rock inside the planet swells and explodes. Some of this lava might also have come from rocks that were melted by the heat of the crashing meteoroids. Wide, smooth plains separate some of the craters from each other. These flat lands were probably formed by flowing lava that leaked from old volcanoes.

9 Long, steep, rocky cliffs cross Mercury's plains. These **scarps** sometimes zigzag right across craters. Nothing like these scarps has been seen on any other planet. Scientists think that the scarps might have formed as Mercury's core cooled. The cooling caused the planet to shrink and bring about these scarps.

10 Mercury is a rocky world without water or weather. Its atmosphere is so weak it is insignificant. There have never been any rivers, oceans, or wind to change its surface. It has remained the same for billions of years. Scientists believe Mercury has changed very little from when it was first formed.

11 Given this information, scientists are quite puzzled over the possibility of ice on Mercury. **Radar** reports show reflective areas on Mercury's north and south poles. Scientists wonder how there could be ice on a planet with no water or weather. Also, the extreme high temperatures and closeness to the sun would not support the idea of ice. If ice is there, the poles would have to always face away from the sun.

NASA has plans to further explore the possibility of ice on Mercury. A Mercury mission is planned for 2004. The Messenger spacecraft will fly past Earth, Venus, and Mercury. Then Messenger will enter into Mercury's orbit to collect information. The mission will end in 2010. At that point, scientists hope to have new information about both Mercury and its neighboring planet, Venus. **12**

C. Finding the Main Idea

Highlight or circle the main idea in each paragraph. Remember that the main idea of a paragraph is often the first or last sentence in that paragraph. Other times, the main idea has to be pieced together from more than one sentence.

D. Making a Timeline

Place two important dates from this lesson on the timeline. Write two or three words to identify the importance of each date.

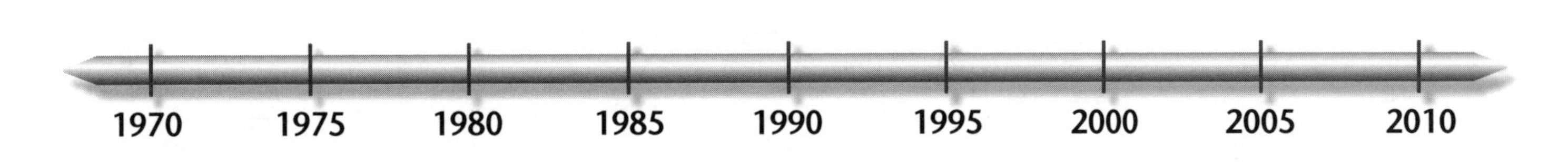

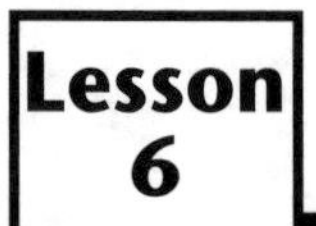

Mercury

E. Using Context Clues

Find the following four vocabulary words in the article. The words and sentences around each word give a clue to its meaning. Use these clues to write a meaning for each word. For each vocabulary word, describe one clue that you used.

1. unaided

Meaning: ______________________

____

____

Clue: ______________________

____

2. lava

Meaning: ______________________

____

____

Clue: ______________________

____

3. scarps

Meaning: ______________________

____

____

Clue: ______________________

____

4. twilight

Meaning: ______________________

____

____

Clue: ______________________

____

F. Reading for Details

Reread the two paragraphs identified below. Then, complete the main idea/detail webs.

Paragraph # 2

Main Idea: ______________________

____

____

Which one?

What?

How much?

Paragraph # 12

Main Idea: ______________________

____

____

What?

When?

Where?

Mercury

G. Giving Short Answers

Use complete sentences to answer these questions.

1. Could there be ice on Mercury? Why or why not?

____

____

2. What is the temperature range on Mercury?

____

____

3. How large is Mercury? How far from the sun is it?

____

____

H. Making a Diagram

Draw a picture showing Mercury's surface. Include craters, valleys, plains, and scarps. Label these features.

Venus

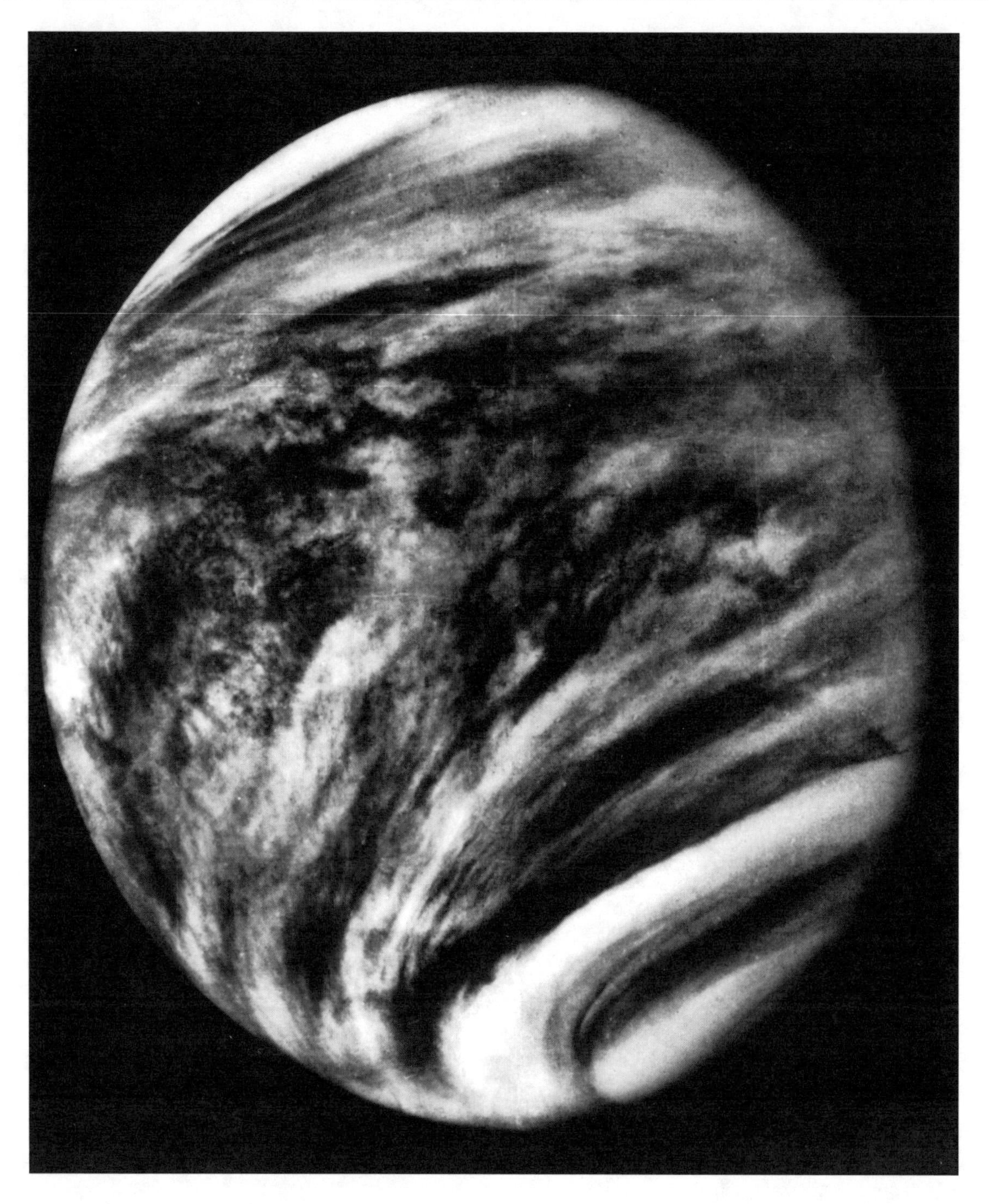

A view of Venus from 450,000 miles away shows the swirl of clouds at Venus' South Pole.

Venus

Lesson 7

A. Setting the Stage

Read the first two and last two paragraphs of this lesson. Write four nouns or phrases that appear to be key ideas.

1.	2.	3.	4.

B. Discussing the Background

Reread the last two paragraphs of Lesson 6. As a group, discuss the relationship between Lesson 6 and Lesson 7.

Words to Know

- stable
- insulator
- sulfur crystals
- haze
- sulfuric acid
- carbon dioxide
- trace
- greenhouse effect

1 Venus is the second planet from the sun. It is 67 million miles away. Venus' orbit is between that of Earth and Mercury. Venus is nearer to Earth than any other planet. It is always covered by clouds that reflect a great amount of sunlight. Since Venus is fairly close to Earth, it looks very bright. It is the easiest planet to see in the sky.

2 At night, Venus shines more brightly than anything except the moon. Some people call Venus the "evening star" or "morning star" because it shines so brightly. At dawn, Venus also shines brightly. Sometimes it is the last point of brightness seen in the morning sky. The Romans thought this planet was a pretty object. They named it Venus after their goddess of love and beauty.

3 Venus is also very hot. It is hotter than Mercury, although it is almost twice as far from the sun. Unlike Mercury, the temperature on Venus is **stable.** The temperature on Venus, both day and night, is around 465°C (870°F). The thick clouds covering Venus act like a blanket or **insulator.** The clouds trap the sun's heat and keep the energy from leaking out into space.

4 The clouds that cover Venus are pale yellow. The color is from **sulfur crystals.** The yellow clouds completely hide the planet's surface. Its cloud covering is actually made of three layers. These layers are stacked one above the other with clear layers in between.

The cloud layers vary from thin to thick. The top layer reaches a height of about 40 miles. It is several miles thick. This layer is just a thin **haze.** Very strong winds blow this layer of clouds around the planet once every four days. The second layer of clouds reaches 36 miles high. This section is even thinner than the first. It is also slower moving. The third layer is 30 miles above Venus' surface. Its thick clouds give off showers of **sulfuric acid.** This strong chemical can eat away rocks. Thunder and lightning occur constantly in this layer. **5**

The cloud layers completely cover Venus. This covering makes it difficult to see the planet. From Earth, no telescope can look through this thick covering. Because of these clouds, people did not know much about the surface of Venus until the 1960s. Between 1962 and 1984, many United States and Russian spacecraft peeked under these clouds. Much has been learned about Venus because of these spacecraft. **6**

In 1989, the Magellan spacecraft visited Venus. This mission produced detailed maps of Venus' surface using radar. **7**

In October 1997, the Cassini spacecraft headed off toward Saturn. The mission is a joint effort of NASA, the European Space Agency, and the Italian Space Agency. Cassini is scheduled to arrive at Saturn in 2004. In August of 1999, Cassini had passed the inner planets including Venus. Cassini sent Venus data back to Earth. Through this data scientists learned more about Venus both within and below the clouds. **8**

Below the clouds, Venus' surface is a bare, baking desert. Most of the planet is flat with many shallow craters. There are two highland areas. One is about the size of Australia. The tallest point on Venus is almost seven miles high. Pictures show dusty, brown rocks. They are so hot that they seem to glow. There is no water on Venus. If there were, the high temperatures would turn it into steam at once. **9**

10

Venus' atmosphere is made mostly of **carbon dioxide** (a heavy colorless gas). There are only **traces** oxygen. Carbon dioxide acts like the glass in a greenhouse. It lets in the sun's rays but traps the heat close to the planet's surface. This **greenhouse effect** causes Venus to become hotter and hotter.

Astronomers have called Venus the "sister planet" of Earth. This comparison is made because the planets are almost the same in size, density, and gravity. Venus' orbit is nearest to Earth. Also, Venus' air is made up of some of the same gases, as well. **11**

Still, these sister planets are really more different than alike. First, days go by very slowly on Venus. It turns the slowest on its axis of all the planets. It also spins backwards. This means that on Venus the sun rises in the west and sets in the east. Venus takes longer to spin on its axis than it does to travel around the sun. So, a day on Venus is longer that its year! Venus' day lasts 243 Earth days. Venus' year lasts 225 Earth days. Also, the atmosphere there is very heavy. It weighs 90 times that of Earth's. **12**

Venus probably once had large bodies of water like Earth but the water all boiled away. Now, Venus is very dry. Earth was able to keep its water because it is farther away from the sun. **13**

Life as we know it does not exist on Venus. As you already know, the air on Venus contains carbon dioxide, which plants need to live. However, it is much too hot on Venus for plants or animals like those on Earth to survive. **14**

C. Finding the Main Idea

Highlight or circle the main idea in each paragraph. Remember that the main idea of a paragraph is often the first or last sentence in that paragraph. Other times, the main idea has to be pieced together from more than one sentence.

D. Making a Timeline

Place two important dates from this lesson on the timeline. Write two or three words to identify the importance of each date.

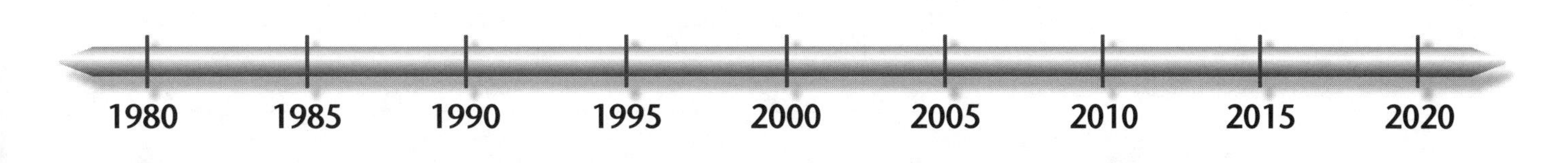

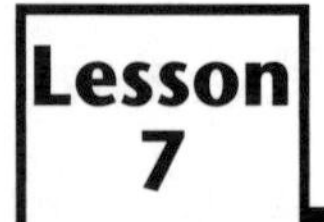

E. Using Context Clues

Find the following four vocabulary words in the article. The words and sentences around each word give a clue to its meaning. Use these clues to write a meaning for each word. For each vocabulary word, describe one clue that you used.

1. stable

Meaning: ______________________

____

____

Clue: ______________________

____

2. insulator

Meaning: ______________________

____

____

Clue: ______________________

____

3. sulfuric acid

Meaning: ______________________

____

____

Clue: ______________________

____

4. greenhouse effect

Meaning: ______________________

____

____

Clue: ______________________

____

F. Reading for Details

Reread the two paragraphs identified below. Then, complete the main idea/detail webs.

Paragraph # 2

Main Idea: ______________________

____

____

When?

What?

Why named Venus?

Paragraph # 9

Main Idea: ______________________

____

____

What?

How high?

How hot?

Venus

G. Giving Short Answers

Use complete sentences to answer these questions.

1. What is the temperature like on Venus? Give specific details.

____

____

2. Why is the surface of Venus difficult to see?

____

____

3. Why is Venus called a "sister planet" to Earth?

____

____

H. Making a Diagram

Use markers, crayons, or colored pencils to draw a color picture of Venus. Show the cloud layers in your picture.

Lesson 8 Earth

This fantastic view of Earth was photographed from the *Apollo 17* spacecraft in December of 1972. The photograph shows Earth from the Mediterranean Sea to the Antarctic south polar ice cap.

Earth

Lesson 8

A. Setting the Stage

Read the first two and last two paragraphs of this lesson. Write four nouns or phrases that appear to be key ideas.

1.	2.	3.	4.

B. Discussing the Background

Reread the last two paragraphs of Lesson 7. As a group, discuss the relationship between Lesson 7 and Lesson 8.

Words to Know

- mass
- rotation
- molten
- mantle
- crust
- continent
- tremor
- water vapor
- magnetic field

1 The third planet from the sun is Earth. It is the fifth largest planet. Long ago, people thought that Earth was the center of the universe. They believed the sun, moon, stars, and planets all revolved around Earth. Now scientists know the sun is the center of the solar system. Earth is just one of many planets in the solar system. Yet, it is very special because it is the only place where scientists know life to exist.

2 The earth is 93 million miles away from the sun. At this distance it gets just the right amount of heat and light. It does not bake like Mercury and Venus. Neither does it freeze like the farthest planets from the sun. Earth's atmosphere contains oxygen. This is the gas that people and all other animals breathe. Earth's air also contains carbon dioxide for plants to breathe. The planet has water for plants and animals to drink. Earth is a perfect place for living things.

3 Seventy-one percent of Earth's surface is covered with water. Earth is the only planet where scientists know water to exist as a liquid. Liquid water is needed for human life. The bodies of water also help to keep Earth's temperature stable.

4 Earth's mass is about 6,600 million trillion tons. Its mass causes it to have a force of gravity that pulls everything toward the planet's center. Earth's gravity is powerful enough to keep a huge air mass close to its surface.

Lesson 8

Earth

Earth revolves around the sun faster than all the planets except Mercury and Venus. It takes the earth 365 days to travel once around the sun. As the planet orbits, different parts face the sun. This condition produces the four seasons. It takes Earth 24 hours to spin once on its axis. This **rotation** equals one day. Research suggests Earth's rotations have changed over the last 900 million years. Earth used to have 481 days that were each 18-hours long. **5**

People see the earth's surface every day. The earth below the surface is not nearly as well known. Scientists' best guess is that Earth is made of several layers. This guess is based on measurements scientists have made on Earth's surface. The first layer has two parts. The inner core is about 800 miles thick and is probably made of solid metal. Around the inner core is an outer core of molten metal. This outer, liquid core can reach temperatures of about 6,100°C (11,000°F). It is about as hot as the sun's surface. **6**

The second layer of Earth is called the **mantle,** which is the middle layer of a rocky planet. It is about 1,800 miles thick. It is made of hot, thick rock. The part of this rock closest to the **crust** is so hot that it acts like taffy. The mantle will bend under a steady force. If it is hit hard, however, it will break. **7**

The last layer of the earth is its crust. The crust is a fairly thin layer of hard rocks near the surface. It is about 22 miles thick under the land and about five miles thick under the water. Lightweight rocks make up the crust. **Continents** and oceans are found here. Earth's crust is made of several separate plates. These plates float on top of the hot mantle below. Shifting of the plates causes earthquakes and ground **tremors.** **8**

Beyond the crust is the atmosphere. It floats above the surface and surrounds the whole planet. Most of Earth's atmosphere contains the gases nitrogen and oxygen. Together, scientists call these gases *air.* Air also has **water vapor** that helps make rain and traps heat from the sun. Water vapor gives living things the warmth and wetness they need. Earth's atmosphere protects plants and animals from getting too much sunshine during the day. It also keeps in enough heat so that living things do not freeze at night. **9**

Earth is like a giant magnet. An invisible **magnetic field** surrounds the planet. Like a bar magnet, Earth's surface has magnetic north and south poles. Earth's magnetic force extends thousands of miles into space. **10**

Earth

Like the other planets, Earth reflects light from the sun. When seen from the moon, Earth shines in the sky. It appears with white clouds, blue oceans, and red-brown continents. In 1972, NASA astronauts took some beautiful pictures of Earth while they were on the moon. These pictures, along with others, show how beautiful Earth looks from space. **11**

One day, humans will also probably be able to look at Earth from Mars. Mars is the next planet in order going away from the sun. The beautiful details of Earth will be less easily seen from Mars. The average distance of about 50 million miles between the two planets makes it hard to see clearly from one to the other. **12**

C. Finding the Main Idea

Highlight or circle the main idea in each paragraph. Remember that the main idea of a paragraph is often the first or last sentence in that paragraph. Other times, the main idea has to be pieced together from more than one sentence.

D. Making a Timeline

Place one important date from this lesson on the timeline. Also place one important date from Lesson 7. Write two or three words to identify the importance of each date.

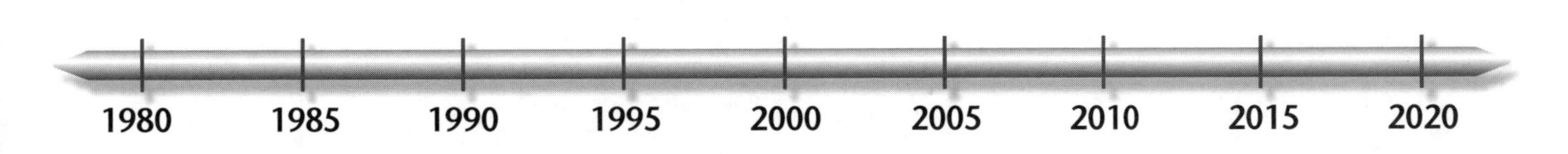

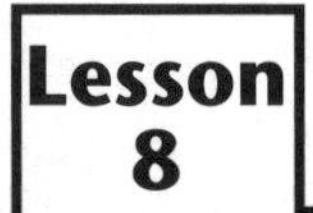

E. Reading for Details

Reread the two paragraphs identified below. Then, complete the main idea/detail webs.

Paragraph # 4

Main Idea: ____________________

____

____

Weighs how much?

Pulls what?

Where?

Paragraph # 9

Main Idea: ____________________

____

____

Where?

How many gases?

Which ones?

F. Making a Diagram

Draw and label the layers of the earth.

Getting Meaning from Context

Unit 3

This photo of Saturn, taken by a telescope in 1968, shows the planet and its rings.

Another helpful tool in reading is called context. Context is the way words are combined to give meaning. Context, then, is really a clue that helps you understand what you read. Read this paragraph:

> The terrain of the planet Mercury has remained the same for billions of years. It is covered with many rocks and craters. Large mountains and wide, smooth plains can also be found there. Steep, rocky cliffs cross Mercury's plains. There have never been any rivers, oceans, or wind to wear down this planet's rocky *terrain.*

While you might not recognize the word *terrain,* the way in which it is used above should help you understand its meaning. The following words serve as context clues:

> covered with many rocks and craters; large mountains; wide, smooth plains; steep, rocky cliffs; rivers, oceans, or wind

These words act as clues in the paragraph. The context words tell you that *terrain* means land or surface.

Context clues can also be used when filling in a blank with a word that has been left out of a sentence. The other words in the sentence give clues to the missing word.

Seeing a new word in context is one of the most helpful ways to figure out what the word means. As you read the lessons in this unit, use context clues to get the meaning of words you do not know.

Lesson 9

Mars

This satellite view of Mars shows the valleys and trenches on the planet's surface.

Mars

Lesson 9

A. Setting the Stage

Read the first two and last two paragraphs of this lesson. Write four nouns or phrases that appear to be key ideas.

1.	2.	3.	4.

B. Discussing the Background

Reread the last two paragraphs of Lesson 8. As a group, discuss the relationship between Lesson 8 and Lesson 9.

Words to Know
ancient
polar caps
ultraviolet
probe
canyon
channel

1 Mars is the fourth planet from the sun. It moves in an egg-shaped orbit at a distance of 142 million miles from the sun. Mars has a nickname: the Red Planet. About every two years, Mars shines brightly in the sky. At that time, its red light seems brighter than that of any star. Thousands of years ago, this red light made **ancient** people think of blood and war. The Romans named this red planet after their god of war, Mars.

2 Mars is the third smallest planet in the solar system. Being one of Earth's closest neighbors, people often study the planet. In some ways, Mars is like Earth and in other ways it is very different. Mars is about one-tenth as big as Earth. Yet, Mars has as much land as Earth. Much of Earth is covered with large oceans. Mars has none. In fact, Mars has no bodies of water at all. It never rains there. In the summer, wild dust storms sometimes cover the whole planet.

3 Mars has seasons like Earth's, but they last twice as long. Days are about the same length as on Earth—24 hours. Mars has a north and south pole—just as Earth does. These poles are covered with white **polar caps.** These caps look like the earth's ice caps. As on Earth, each polar cap grows bigger in winter and shrinks in summer. During the middle of a summer day, parts of Mars can warm up to 27°C (80°F). At the poles, the temperature drops as low as –101°C (–214°F). This is colder than anywhere on Earth.

People could not breathe on Mars. The air is mostly made of carbon dioxide. Mars' air is almost 100 times thinner than Earth's air. Such thin air cannot protect people from the sun's deadly **ultraviolet** rays. Human blood would boil on Mars! 4

Many scientists believe that Mars gets enough light and energy to support life. Also, the air on the planet is made of the gases living things need: nitrogen, carbon dioxide, and oxygen. Data suggests that Mars might once have had flowing water. Mars does have water now in the form of ice and vapor. This means that simple plant life probably could exist on Mars. 5

Mars is orbited by two small, oblong moons. Phobos, meaning *fear,* is the larger of the two. It is 14 miles across. It has many craters and grooves. Deimos, meaning *terror,* is about half as big. Both are hard and lumpy. Scientists think these moons were once asteroids. The gravity of Mars probably captured them long ago. 6

Most of scientists' early knowledge about Mars has come from three space **probes.** These spacecraft were sent from Earth to explore the planet. Mariner 9 took the first clear pictures of Mars in 1971. In 1976, Viking 1 and 2 set landers down upon the planet's surface. These space probes sent back thousands of pictures of Mars. 7

These pictures showed that Mars is mostly a dry, rocky desert. It is covered with stones and dusty reddish soil. The soil contains a kind of rusted iron, which makes the planet look red. Its surface has many craters and plains like the moon. There are giant **canyons** and huge volcanoes. Mars' biggest canyon is known as Mariner Valley. It is ten times longer and three times deeper than the Grand Canyon. The largest volcano on Mars, Mount Olympus, looks like a huge mountain of cooled lava. It is 15 miles high and about 50 miles wide. New York City could easily fit inside. 8

The Mariner and Viking pictures also showed winding **channels** that look like dried-up river beds. These channels may have been carved by mighty flowing rivers long ago. Many scientists believe that Mars was once much wetter and warmer than it is today. Most of Mars' water might now be frozen and buried deep underground. 9

On July 4, 1997, after a 20-year absence, NASA landed a spacecraft on Mars. Mars Pathfinder took new pictures and did tests. Global Surveyor entered Mars' orbit on September 11, 1997. The spacecraft is still orbiting the red planet and sending an ongoing stream of data back to Earth. 10

Along with the spacecraft, the Hubble Telescope collects information about Mars. In 1996, Hubble captured a rare polar dust storm. In 1997, Hubble photographed the start of the orbit of NASA's Global Surveyor as it began its journey around Mars. **11**

This new information is being collected, studied, and calculated. Scientists are beginning to update and replace the data collected in the 1970s. **12**

The more scientists learn about Mars, the more likely it is that people will visit Mars. Right now, NASA has a long-range goal for the planet: a Martian outpost in the 2020s or 2030s. **13**

Although NASA is very interested in Mars, other planets are also being studied. The outer planets, beginning with Jupiter, are involved in ongoing spacecraft flybys and data collections. **14**

C. Finding the Main Idea

Highlight or circle the main idea in each paragraph. Remember that the main idea of a paragraph is often the first or last sentence in that paragraph. Other times, the main idea has to be pieced together from more than one sentence.

D. Making a Timeline

Place three important dates from this lesson on the timeline. Write two or three words to identify the importance of each date.

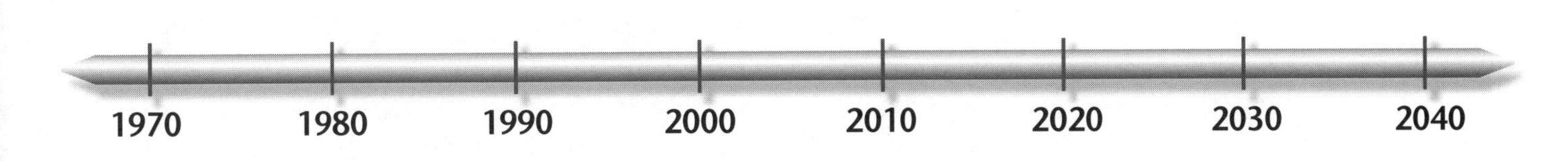

E. Using Context Clues

Find the following four vocabulary words in the article. The words and sentences around each word give a clue to its meaning. Use these clues to write a meaning for each word. For each vocabulary word, describe one clue that you used.

1. ancient

Meaning: ______________________

____

____

Clue: ______________________

____

2. probes

Meaning: ______________________

____

____

Clue: ______________________

____

3. channels

Meaning: ______________________

____

____

Clue: ______________________

____

4. canyons

Meaning: ______________________

____

____

Clue: ______________________

____

F. Reading for Details

Reread the two paragraphs identified below. Then, complete the main idea/detail webs.

Paragraph # 5

Main Idea: ______________________

____

____

- How?
- Breathe what?
- Water from where?

Paragraph # 8

Main Idea: ______________________

____

____

- Why red?
- What land formations?
- Which ones are biggest?

G. Using Context to Make Choices

Read each selection below. Chose the best word to replace the word in italics or to fill in the blank. Use context clues for help. Circle the letter of the correct answer.

1. It is likely that people will visit Mars. A *Martian* outpost is planned for the 2020s or 2030s.

   a. alien b. distant c. on Mars d. on Earth

2. Mars' tallest volcano is 15 miles high. It is the tallest known volcano in the solar system. It __________ three times higher than Earth's highest mountain, Mount Everest.

   a. rises b. spurts lava c. explodes d. crashes

3. The best pictures of Mars came from the Viking 1 and 2 spacecrafts. They *transmitted* bits of information back to Earth by radio signals. Computers here on Earth turned the information into pictures.

   a. gathered b. received c. circled d. sent

4. Scientists think there was once flowing water on Mars. The Viking space probes did __________ water, ice, and vapor on the planet. The Viking also found channels that may be dried-up river beds.

   a. find b. melt c. collect d. search

5. The surface of Mars is dry and rough. Much of it looks like the Arizona desert. Iron-rich stones are *strewn* over the dusty, reddish soil.

   a. broken b. blown c. scattered d. piled

H. Making a Diagram

Draw a diagram of Mars and its two orbiting moons. Label the diagram.

Lesson 10 Jupiter

This artist's concept of Jupiter shows the planet and its moons on its 12-year journey around the sun. Also visible is the Great Red Spot on Jupiter's surface.

Jupiter

Lesson 10

A. Setting the Stage

Read the first two and last two paragraphs of this lesson. Write four nouns or phrases that appear to be key ideas.

1.	2.	3.	4.

B. Discussing the Background

Reread the last two paragraphs of Lesson 9. As a group, discuss the relationship between Lesson 9 and Lesson 10.

Words to Know
giant planets
erupt
confirm
detect
debris

1 Jupiter is the first and largest of the four **giant planets**. The others are Saturn, Uranus, and Neptune. These planets are called the "gas giants" because they consist mostly of gases. They are very different from the rocky, land planets. Jupiter is a huge ball of liquid and gas. It might not have any solid surface at all.

2 Jupiter is easily the biggest planet in the solar system. It is larger and heavier than all of the other planets in the solar system put together. Straight through its center, it is more than eleven times as wide as Earth. More than 1,300 Earths could fit inside Jupiter. Because of its huge size, the Romans named Jupiter after the king of their gods.

3 This huge planet is completely wrapped in clouds. The clouds reflect large amounts of sunlight. The reflecting makes Jupiter shine brighter than any planet except Venus. When astronomers look at Jupiter, they see the tops of brown, yellow, blue-green, gray, red, and orange clouds. These clouds form bands as the planet spins very fast. The spinning planet causes these cloud bands to swirl and form huge, powerful storms. Astronomers think that Jupiter's famous Great Red Spot is a constant storm of swirling gases. This storm is larger than the earth and has raged for hundreds of years.

4 Jupiter is made mostly of hydrogen gas. It also contains some helium. Jupiter's clouds have traces of methane, ammonia, water vapor, and other gases. Still, there must be other chemicals to give the clouds their bright colors. Scientists believe Jupiter has a rocky core. They think the core is about the size of Earth and is surrounded by hot liquid hydrogen.

Jupiter

Below the thick cloud covering, Jupiter is a hot planet. It gives off more heat than it receives from the sun. It also sends out radio signals and X-rays. Scientists think that Jupiter's heat comes more from its own center than from the sun. Jupiter, then, is different from most of the other planets. It is more like a star than a planet, since all the other planets except Neptune get all their heat from the sun. **5**

In 1979, Voyager I discovered that a narrow ring surrounds Jupiter. The ring is made of many tiny particles. These bits whirl around the planet. They reflect sunlight like specks of dust in a beam of light. Scientists are not sure where these particles come from. A guess is that they are ashes coming from a volcano on one of Jupiter's moons. **6**

There are sixteen known moons that orbit Jupiter. Io, Europa, Ganymede, and Callisto are the four biggest and brightest. They were discovered by the Italian astronomer, Galileo Galilei, in 1610. Voyager 1 took pictures of these moons in 1979. Scientists have spent years studying the information sent back by this space probe. **7**

Io and Europa are about the same size as Earth's moon. Some of Voyager's pictures show large and active volcanoes on Io. These volcanoes **erupt** at speeds of up to 932 miles per hour. Europa shines the brightest. Its surface is smooth and icy. **8**

Ganymede is bigger than the planet Mercury. Ganymede is the largest known moon in the solar system. Callisto is almost as large as Mercury and looks very old. It is covered with craters that look like they have not changed in 4 billion years. Both moons seem to be half water and half rock. **9**

In October of 1989, the Galileo Project launched off the shuttle Atlantis. Over the next six years, the Galileo probe made its way to Jupiter. In December of 1995, the probe and orbiter separated. The Galileo orbiter became the first spacecraft to enter Jupiter's orbit. The probe became the first spacecraft to enter Jupiter's atmosphere. These two spacecraft updated and **confirmed** Voyager I data. They discovered far less water on Jupiter than estimated by Voyager. Wind speeds were **detected** at faster than 400 miles per hour. Io's surface looks different due to ongoing volcanic action since Voyager's flyby in 1979. **10**

The Galileo Project also collected a great deal of new data about Jupiter and its satellites. New information included the first real data about the makeup of a gas planet. Jupiter has less lightning activity than Earth. However, the individual lightning cracks are about ten times stronger than on Earth. The Galileo Project found evidence of a liquid water ocean under Europa's surface. **11**

Jupiter

Lesson 10

12 In 1994, the KAO (Kuiper Airborne Observatory) captured a collision on Jupiter. The comet Shoemaker-Levy 9 collided with Jupiter. An entire year later, KAO still reported collision **debris** in Jupiter's atmosphere.

13 The KAO was a powerful telescope system mounted in a C-141 military cargo plane. The plane flew at 41,000 feet, just above most of Earth's atmosphere. From this position, KAO could see better than any telescope on Earth. The KAO was retired in 1995. A replacement, SOFIA (Stratospheric Observatory for Infrared Astronomy) should be ready in 2002.

14 Voyager also collected data on Jupiter's giant next door neighbor, Saturn. When a spacecraft goes all the way to Jupiter, it makes sense to visit Saturn while in the area. Of course, in the area is relative. The trip to Jupiter is about 400,000,000 miles from Earth. The trip from Jupiter to Saturn is about the same distance. In other words, Jupiter is half way to Saturn. Only in space language would 400,000,000 miles be considered in the area! In fact, such distances exist only in space travel.

C. Finding the Main Idea

Highlight or circle the main idea in each paragraph. Remember that the main idea of a paragraph is often the first or last sentence in that paragraph. Other times, the main idea has to be pieced together from more than one sentence.

D. Making a Timeline

Place two important dates from this lesson on the timeline. Write two or three words to identify the importance of each date.

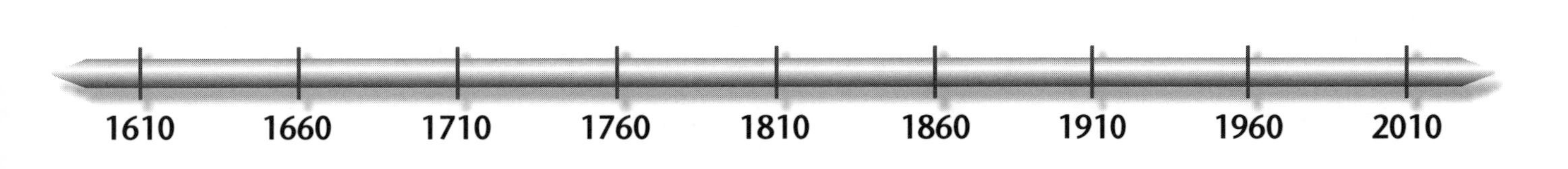

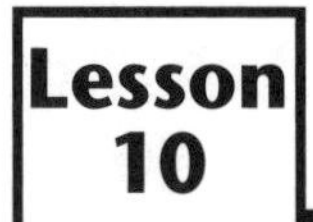

E. Using Context Clues

Find the following four vocabulary words in the article. The words and sentences around each word give a clue to its meaning. Use these clues to write a meaning for each word. For each vocabulary word, describe one clue that you used.

1. giant planets

Meaning: ______________________________

____

____

Clue: ______________________________

____

2. erupt

Meaning: ______________________________

____

____

Clue: ______________________________

____

3. detect

Meaning: ______________________________

____

____

Clue: ______________________________

____

4. debris

Meaning: ______________________________

____

____

Clue: ______________________________

____

F. Reading for Details

Reread the two paragraphs identified below. Then, complete the main idea/detail webs.

Paragraph # 2

Main Idea: ______________________________

____

____

How big?

How wide?

How many Earths can fit?

Paragraph # 12

Main Idea: ______________________________

____

____

When?

How was it seen?

What evidence remains?

Jupiter

G. Using Context to Make Choices

Read each selection below. Chose the best word to replace the word in italics or to fill in the blank. Use context clues for help. Circle the letter next to the correct answer.

1. The "gas giants" *consist* mostly of gases.

   a. are made **b.** are lost **c.** lose **d.** capture

2. Jupiter spins so fast that its cloud bands swirl. This causes many powerful storms. The planet's strong __________ atmosphere probably formed the Great Red Spot.

   a. cloudy **b.** gassy **c.** swirling **d.** heavy

3. Deep below Jupiter's surface, pressure is very high. It is so high that hydrogen is *compressed* into a liquid form.

   a. squashed **b.** mixed **c.** boiled **d.** melted

4. Callisto is one of Jupiter's sixteen moons. It is a very old and *battered* satellite. It is almost completely covered by craters. Its beaten surface was probably bombarded by comets and rocks. Large meteorites also likely slammed into Callisto.

   a. smoothed **b.** heated **c.** melted **d.** hit or beaten

5. Io, one of Jupiter's moons, seems to be __________ craters. Scientists were surprised to see no Io craters in any of Voyager's pictures. They think that the moon's active volcanoes buried all the craters.

   a. moving **b.** shrinking **c.** lacking **d.** getting deeper

H. Making a Diagram

Draw a picture of Jupiter and its moons.

Saturn

This artist's depiction shows how Saturn might look to astronauts landing on its largest satellite, Titan.

Saturn

Lesson 11

A. Setting the Stage

Read the first two and last two paragraphs of this lesson. Write four nouns or phrases that appear to be key ideas.

1.	2.	3.	4.

B. Discussing the Background

Reread the last two paragraphs of Lesson 10. As a group, discuss the relationship between Lesson 10 and Lesson 11.

Words to Know
rings
microscopic
hollow
dense
enormous
captured asteroid

1 The most eye-catching planet in the solar system is Saturn. Its beautiful **rings** have interested people for hundreds of years. The Italian astronomer Galileo thought they looked like ears, one on each side of Saturn. In 1655, Christian Huygens, a Dutch astronomer, was the first person to see them as rings.

2 Saturn's rings consist of millions of particles of ice, rock, and dust. They orbit the planet at very high speeds. The smallest of these particles are **microscopic** in size. The biggest can be as large as houses. They shine by reflected sunlight. The rings stretch move than 169,000 miles across. They are not even a mile thick. Scientists are not sure how Saturn's rings came to be.

3 Until 1977, people believed Saturn was the only planet with rings. Since then, scientists have discovered rings around Uranus, Jupiter, and Neptune.

4 Saturn is the second largest planet in the solar system. If it were hollow, 755 Earths could fit inside it. The planet is 95 times heavier than Earth. Yet, for its size, it is the lightest planet of all. It is less **dense** than the other planets. Its gases are not packed as tightly together. If Saturn could be dropped into a large enough ocean, it would float!

Saturn

Saturn is smaller and cooler than Jupiter. However, Saturn is like Jupiter in several ways. It is a huge, fast-spinning ball of gas. Like Jupiter, it is made mostly of hydrogen, with some helium. Also, like Jupiter, it probably has a rocky core. Because it spins so fast, its poles are flattened. It sends out radio signals like Jupiter as well. **5**

Thick clouds cover the planet completely. They are always moving around it at hundreds of miles per hour. They form bands around Saturn, just like on Jupiter. These orange and yellow cloud bands are not as colorful or as clear as Jupiter's. They are under a thicker haze. The tops of the clouds are very cold—below 190°C (-300°F). Saturn has areas that look like Jupiter's storms. Details about Saturn are hard to see because of the heavy clouds. **6**

Eighteen known moons orbit Saturn. The largest and most interesting is Titan. It is larger than the planets Mercury and Pluto. Titan is the solar system's second largest moon after Jupiter's Ganymede. A hazy atmosphere made mostly of nitrogen hides Titan's surface. Methane and ethane gas are also in the moon's air. These gases color it reddish orange. Titan is a most unusual moon. It is the only one in the solar system with an atmosphere. Below Titan's thick, hazy atmosphere is a hard surface of rock and ice. Scientists think pools of liquid methane and ethane may exist there. Titan orbits Saturn at a distance of 759,210 miles. **7**

Voyagers 1 and 2 sent pictures of Titan and of Saturn's other moons. These pictures show many craters covering their surfaces. Some are heavily cracked. One of Saturn's moons, Mimas, has a huge crater. It stretches nearly a quarter of the distance across the moon's surface. **8**

Tethys, another of Saturn's moons, is 660 miles wide. It also has an **enormous** crater on its surface. The crater is almost 250 miles across and 10 miles deep. Scientists think that the crater may have formed long ago when Tethys was warmer. A large break, called Ithaca Chasma, extends almost three quarters of the way around the moon. Astronomers believe that as the moon froze, it cracked and caused the huge split. **9**

Phoebe is the farthest of Saturn's moons. It orbits the planet at a distance of more than 8 million miles. It is a very dark and rough satellite measuring about 137 miles across. Phoebe orbits Saturn in a backward direction and in an unusual position. Some astronomers think that it may be a **captured asteroid.** **10**

Saturn

Lesson 11

11 Scientists now know more about Saturn and its moons than ever before. The Voyager 1 and 2 space probes have given scientists many new facts. Still, with all of this data, there is much more to learn about Saturn and its many satellites.

12 Thanks to the Cassini spacecraft, scientists might soon start studying new data about Saturn. Cassini is on its way towards Saturn and is scheduled to arrive in 2004. Cassini will also fly by Saturn's neighboring planet, Uranus.

C. Finding the Main Idea

Highlight or circle the main idea in each paragraph. Remember that the main idea of a paragraph is often the first or last sentence in that paragraph. Other times, the main idea has to be pieced together from more than one sentence.

D. Making a Timeline

Place two important dates from this lesson on the timeline. Write two or three words to identify the importance of each date.

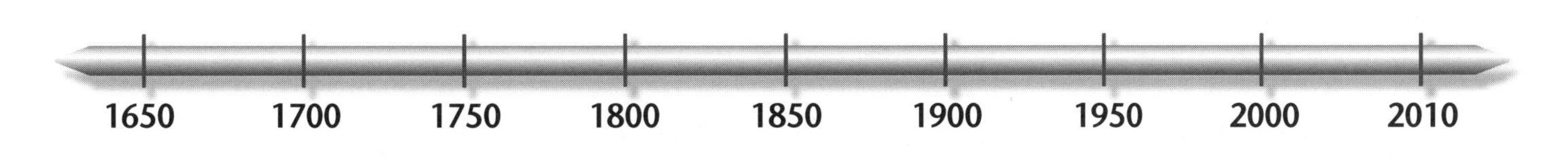

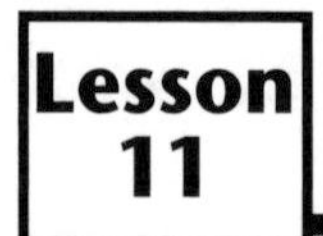

E. Using Context to Make Choices

Read each paragraph below. Chose the best word to replace the word in italics or to fill in the blank. Use context clues for help. Circle the letter next to the correct answer.

1. The smallest particles of Saturn's rings are *microscopic* in size.

   a. huge **b.** small **c.** invisible **d.** normal

2. A thin, glowing cloud of hydrogen *girdles* Saturn and its rings. This cloud is shaped like a huge doughnut. It stretches completely around the planet.

   a. covers **b.** hides **c.** squeezes **d.** circles

3. Like Jupiter, Saturn turns on its axis at a high speed. Days go by quickly on Saturn. Its __________ spin causes a Saturn day to last only about 10.5 hours.

   a. fast **b.** unusual **c.** slow **d.** rocky

4. NASA's spacecraft could not see some of the clouds in Saturn's atmosphere. Some kind of *haze* was hiding them.

   a. moon/satellite **b.** planet **c.** wind or storm **d.** fog or vapor

5. Saturn's moon, Mimas, has a huge crater. It was probably caused by a large meteorite crashing into the surface. Astronomers are surprised that the *collision* did not break Mimas into bits.

   a. object **b.** speed **c.** crash **d.** gas

F. Making a Diagram

Up close, Saturn's rings are not as pretty as they appear from Earth. Draw a tiny segment of a Saturn ring up close.

Putting it All Together

Unit 4

The comet Kohoutek streaks through space. This image was captured by a telescope at the University of Arizona in 1974.

So far, you have practiced the following reading skills:

Getting the main idea

Reading for details

Getting meaning from the context

In this unit, you will practice using all of these skills together. As you know, the main idea is the major point of a paragraph or reading selection. It is the one idea that links all the details together.

The details are the facts that support, explain, or tell about the main idea. Getting the main idea and finding details are easier to do when you understand the context.

As you remember, context refers to the order and combination of the words and sentences in each paragraph and how they are used. Finding the main idea and picking out details are easier to do when you use clues from the context.

As you practice these skills, you will become a better reader.

Uranus

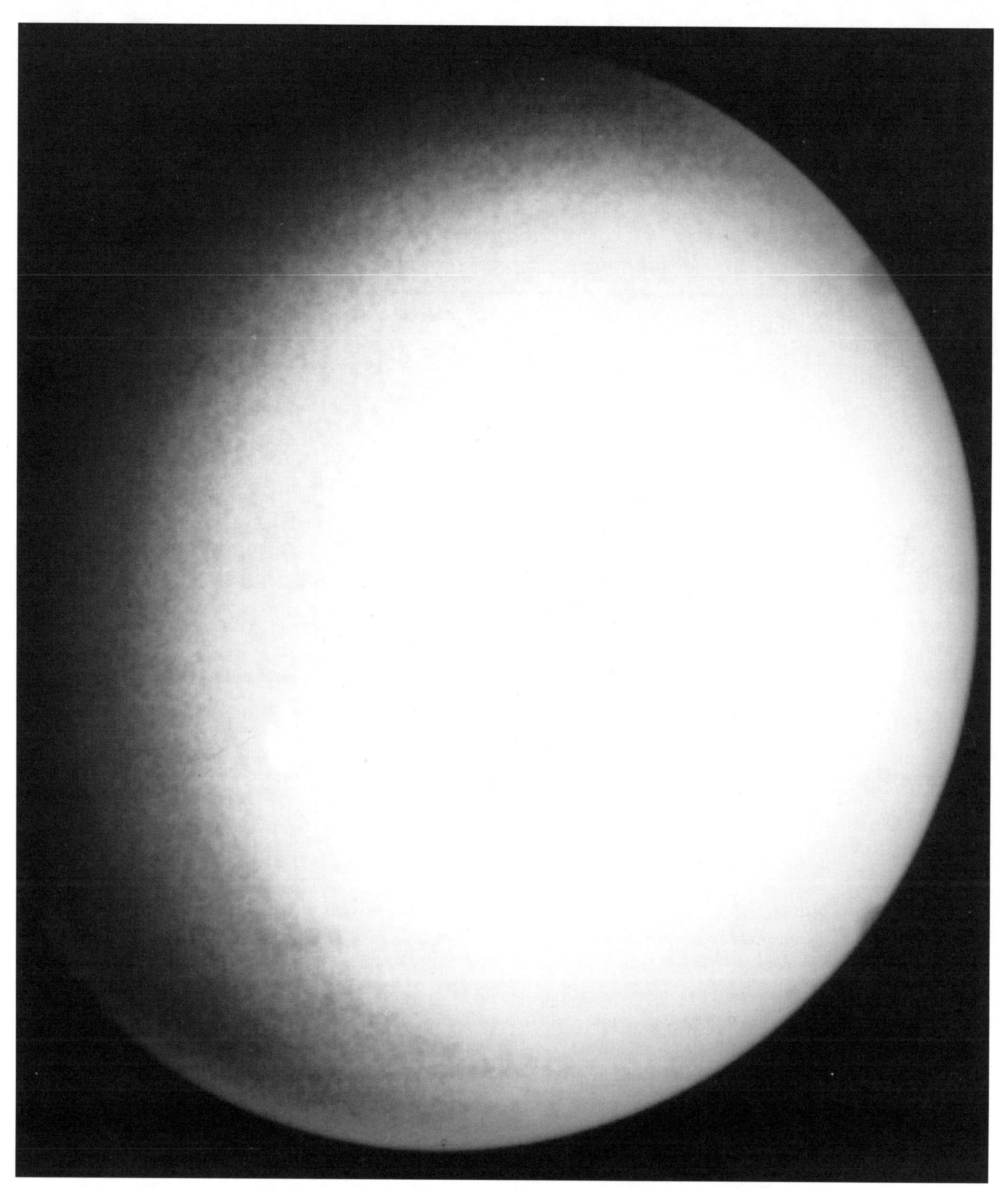

This photo of Uranus was taken by the only spacecraft ever to visit Uranus, *Voyager 2*.

Uranus

Lesson 12

A. Setting the Stage

Read the first two and last two paragraphs of this lesson. Write four nouns or phrases that appear to be key ideas.

1.	2.	3.	4.

B. Discussing the Background

Reread the last two paragraphs of Lesson 11. As a group, discuss the relationship between Lesson 11 and Lesson 12.

Words to Know
astronomy
tilt
observatory
diameter
gullies
jagged
glacier

1 Uranus was discovered in 1781 by Sir William Herschel. Herschel was an English musician. He also had an interest in **astronomy.** He spotted Uranus through a telescope while looking at the sky. At first, Herschel thought that he saw a comet. Uranus became the first planet to be discovered with a telescope.

2 Uranus is the third of the gas giants.The planet is huge even though it is smaller than Jupiter and Saturn. Uranus is 67 times as big as Earth. That means that Uranus is huge compared to Earth. For its size, however, it is a lightweight planet. It is only 14 times as heavy as Earth.

3 Looking through a telescope, Uranus looks like a tiny blue-green star. What astronomers really see are the tops of clouds. These clouds completely surround the planet. They contain methane gas and give Uranus its color.

4 In January of 1986, the space probe Voyager 2 reached Uranus. It sent back new information about the planet. Voyager 2 showed that Uranus has a rocky core. Astronomers think the core is wrapped in thick, icy layers of water, methane, and ammonia. Above these layers is a thin atmosphere of hydrogen, mixed with some helium and neon. The top of the atmosphere is very cold at about –215°C (–355°F).

Uranus

5

Uranus is unusual because it **tilts** on its axis more than any other planet. It looks like a top spinning on its side. Scientists think that an Earth-sized planet might have smashed into Uranus long ago. The crash might have knocked Uranus on its side.

6

Uranus is almost 2 billion miles away from the sun. This distance is 19 times farther the Earth's distance from the sun. Its orbit around the sun is very slow. One year on Uranus equals 84 Earth years. In its path around the sun, parts of Uranus get constant sunlight for 42 years. Other areas of the planet are in total darkness for 42 years. The planet spins on its axis so fast, however, that one day on Uranus lasts just more than 17 hours.

7

In 1977, astronomers discovered nine narrow rings circling Uranus. Their discovery was made using NASA's KAO (Kuiper Airborne **Observatory**) from high above the earth's atmosphere. Astronomers saw that Uranus' rings are one third of the width of Saturn's. They are much less bright because they are not covered with ice. Uranus' rings seem to be made of coal-like chunks of black rock. The smallest of these chunks is about 3 feet across. The largest is about 3,000 feet across.

Before 1986, scientists knew of five moons orbiting Uranus. Their names are Miranda, Ariel, Umbriel, Titania, and Oberon. These moons orbit Uranus in up-and-down paths because Uranus is tilted so much on its side. Astronomers

8

thought that the planet's moons were made of ice mixed with some rock. In 1986, Voyager 2 took pictures of the moons that showed that the moons were made mostly of rock and had craters, valleys, and mountains.

Uranus' two largest moons are Oberon and Titania. They are both about 1,000 miles in **diameter.** Their surfaces have many craters. Oberon has several craters filled with some kind of dark matter. It also has a mountain 12 miles high and many cliffs. Titania also has cliffs as well as **gullies** that might have been left by running water. An unusual frost-like pattern runs next to big cracks in Titania's surface. Scientists are not sure what caused this frost. It looks as if something

9

was sprayed out, froze, and fell to the surface.

10

Umbriel is probably the oldest of Uranus' moons. Umbriel is about 700 miles wide across the middle. Its surface is dark and covered with craters. Umbriel does not show the signs of change that the other moons do. Astronomers are still trying to understand this lack of change.

Uranus

Lesson 12

11 Uranus' brightest moon is Ariel. It is about the same size as Umbriel. It is crossed with wide, curving valleys. As these valleys weave about, they are interrupted by **jagged** canyons. Parts of Ariel's surface look as though they have been smoothed over. Flooding or **glaciers** might have done this.

12 Miranda is the smallest of the five moons Voyager photographed. It is only 300 miles across the middle. It has long curving valleys and grooves. Some of these grooves form V shapes. Others form oval patterns that look like racetracks. Miranda has high areas covered with craters, like Earth's own moon. It also has cliffs towering ten times higher than the sides of the Grand Canyon.

13 In 1986, the Voyager spacecraft also found ten new Uranus moons! More recently, in 1997, two additional Uranus satellites were found using the Hubble Space Telescope. None of these satellites has a regular shape. Eighteen satellites were known to orbit Uranus in the year 2000. Perhaps scientists will learn even more about Uranus and all its moons in the future.

C. Finding the Main Idea

Highlight or circle the main idea in each paragraph. Remember that the main idea of a paragraph is often the first or last sentence in that paragraph. Other times, the main idea has to be pieced together from more than one sentence.

D. Making a Timeline

Place two important dates from this lesson on the timeline. Write two or three words to identify the importance of each date.

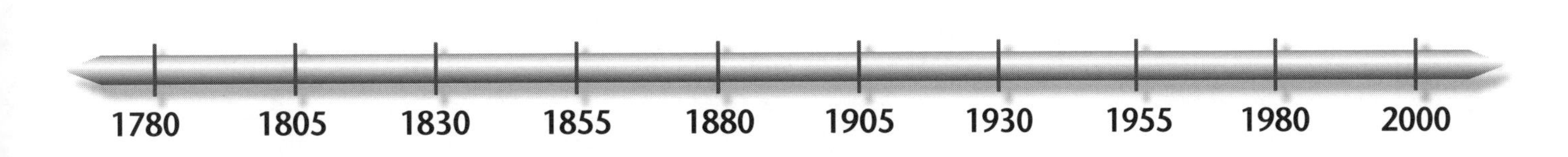

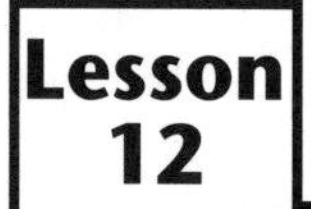
Lesson 12

Uranus

E. Using Context Clues

Find the following four vocabulary words in the article. The words and sentences around each word give a clue to its meaning. Use these clues to write a meaning for each word. For each vocabulary word, describe one clue that you used.

1. observatory

Meaning: ______________________________

____

____

Clue: ______________________________

____

2. diameter

Meaning: ______________________________

____

____

Clue: ______________________________

____

3. gullies

Meaning: ______________________________

____

____

Clue: ______________________________

____

4. jagged

Meaning: ______________________________

____

____

Clue: ______________________________

____

F. Reading for Details

Reread the two paragraphs identified below. Then, complete the main idea/detail webs.

Paragraph # 2

Main Idea: ______________________________

____

____

- How big?
- How heavy?
- Why called lightweight?

Paragraph # 13

Main Idea: ______________________________

____

____

- What did Voyager 2 find?
- How were two more moons found?
- When will scientists learn more?

G. Using Words to Know

Some words are missing from the sentences below. Fill in each blank with the correct word from the Words to Know box on the first page of the lesson. Use context clues.

1. Rough parts of the moon's surface might have been smoothed over by a ____________________ , a large moving body of ice that flattens everything in its way.

2. Sharp, pointed rocks form huge valleys on Ariel. Pictures of these ____________________ rocks were captured by the space probe *Voyager 2.*

3. Sir William Herschel practiced ____________________ . He liked to study the stars, planets, and other objects in the sky. His work led him to discover Uranus.

4. Some astronomers think that an Earth-sized planet crashed into Uranus long ago. The crash could have knocked Uranus on its side. That would explain why the ____________________ of Uranus is so much greater than other planets.

H. Making a Diagram

Below is a sketch of Earth on its axis. Draw a picture of Uranus on its axis.

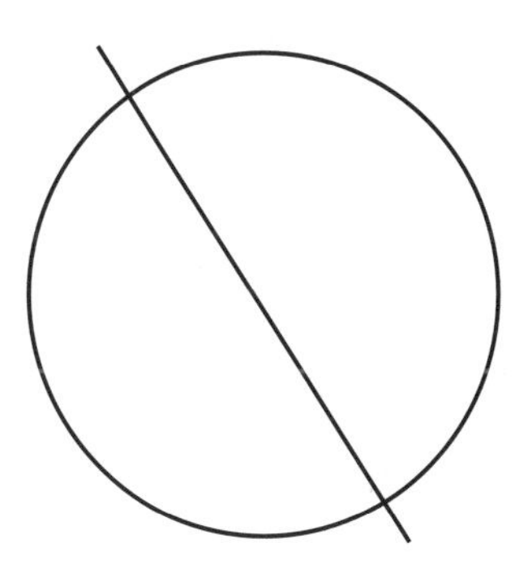

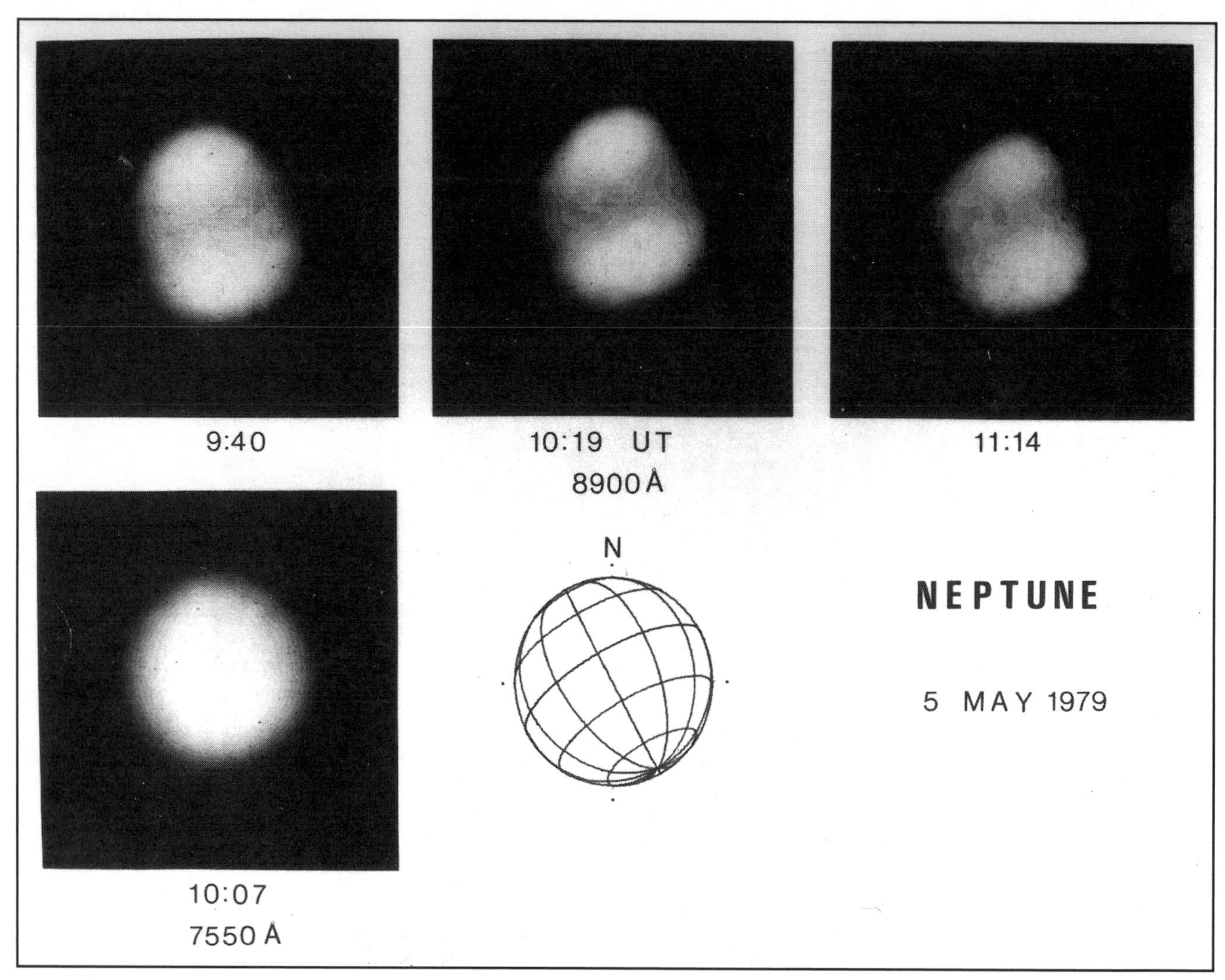

These images of Neptune were captured by a telescope in 1979 at the University of Arizona. The bright areas are high clouds of ice crystals which seem to move as time passes.

Neptune

Lesson 13

A. Setting the Stage

Read the first two and last two paragraphs of this lesson. Write four nouns or phrases that appear to be key ideas.

1.	2.	3.	4.

B. Discussing the Background

Reread the last two paragraphs of Lesson 12. As a group, discuss the relationship between Lesson 12 and Lesson 13.

Words to Know
binoculars
disk
arcs
irregular

1 After Uranus was discovered, scientists began to look at it more closely with their telescopes. They noticed that it did not orbit the sun as expected. Something seemed to be pulling it off course. Astronomers began to wonder if there was yet another unknown planet pulling on Uranus. This planet would likely be even farther from the sun.

2 The answer did not come until 65 years after the discovery of Uranus. On September 23, 1846, Johann G. Galle, a German astronomer, became the first to spot Neptune. He was certain that it was a planet and not some other object.

3 Neptune is the fourth and last of the giant planets in the solar system. Astronomers can see Neptune only with **binoculars** or a telescope. It looks like a small, bright **disk**. The most powerful of telescopes can capture Neptune's light blue color. This coloring is actually the tops of clouds that surround the planet. These cloud tops are very cold, about –230°C (–446°F). Neptune is too far away for astronomers to see any part of its surface. It is almost three billion miles from the earth.

4 Like the other gas planets, Neptune has high winds and large storms. As amazing as it sounds, Neptune's winds reach up to 1,243 km per hour. Scientists believe these winds to be the strongest winds on any planet in the solar system.

Neptune

Scientists can learn only so much about a planet and its satellites through telescopes. To learn more, NASA sent a spacecraft to Neptune. When Voyager 2 reached Neptune in August of 1989, NASA began to learn much more about the planet and its moons. Neptune was the last planet Voyager 2 visited after 12 years of travel through space. **5**

When Voyager 2 visited Neptune, a Great Dark Spot was recorded. In 1994, the Hubble Space Telescope showed that the Great Dark Spot had disappeared. A few months later, the Hubble Space Telescope found a smaller dark spot. These spots either come and go, blow around in the high winds, or become blocked from view. **6**

From Earth, Neptune appears to have faint **arcs** around the planet. Voyager 2 images show that dark solid rings with bright clumps actually circle the planet. **7**

Neptune is often thought of as Uranus' twin. The two planets are almost the same size. Neptune's thick atmosphere contains the same gases as that of Uranus. So far, scientists have detected mostly hydrogen and helium in the planet's atmosphere. Some methane was also found. Scientists think that Neptune was formed like Uranus. Under a thin outer atmosphere, Neptune has thicker layers of gases and liquids. Most of the planet is probably made of hydrogen. Farther inside, Neptune has a layer of water and ammonia ice and a core made of rock and iron. **8**

Like Jupiter, Neptune gives off a lot of heat. In fact, Neptune gives off twice as much heat as it takes in from the sun. This heat is probably left over from when the planet was first formed. It is radiated by the core at a temperature of around 12,632°F (7000°C). Despite this inner heat, Neptune's surface is colder than that of any other planet except Pluto. Neptune's surface stays at a frosty –360°F (–218°C). **9**

Neptune is 2.79 billion miles from the sun. This is 30 times the earth's distance from the sun. It takes almost 165 Earth years for Neptune to travel once around the sun. The planet spins so fast on its axis, however, that a day on Neptune lasts only about 16 hours. If Neptune were hollow, 57 Earths would fit inside. It is more dense than Uranus but less dense than Earth. **10**

Neptune has eight known moons, one large and seven small. Five of these moons were discovered by Voyager 2. Triton, the large moon, is heavier than Earth's moon. It orbits Neptune in only six Earth days. Scientists think that Triton's atmosphere is mostly nitrogen gas. Triton seems to be very close to Neptune. Some astronomers think it may be in danger of being torn apart by Neptune's gravity. **11**

Neptune

12

Nereid, one of Neptune's smaller moons is only 125 miles wide. Nereid is much farther from Neptune than Triton. It takes almost a year for it to orbit the planet. The other six small moons are all quite close to Neptune. They are all even closer than the larger Triton. If Triton is in danger of being torn apart, perhaps these smaller moons are in even greater danger of being gone one day.

13

Humans will not visit Neptune any time soon because it is so far away. Other than Pluto, Neptune is at the outermost point of the solar system. Sometimes, Neptune even moves outside of Pluto for a few years because Pluto has an **irregular** orbit.

C. Finding the Main Idea

Highlight or circle the main idea in each paragraph. Remember that the main idea of a paragraph is often the first or last sentence in that paragraph. Other times, the main idea has to be pieced together from more than one sentence.

D. Making a Timeline

Place three important dates from this lesson on the timeline. Write two or three words to identify the importance of each date.

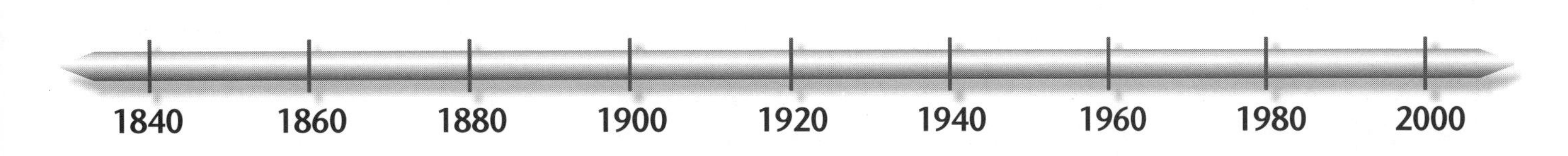

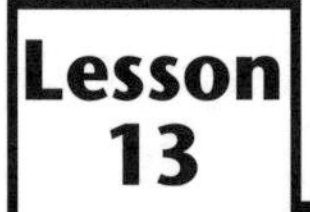

Neptune

E. Using Context Clues

Find the following four vocabulary words in the article. The words and sentences around each word give a clue to its meaning. Use these clues to write a meaning for each word. For each vocabulary word, describe one clue that you used.

1. binoculars

Meaning: ______________________________

____

____

Clue: ______________________________

____

2. arcs

Meaning: ______________________________

____

____

Clue: ______________________________

____

3. disk

Meaning: ______________________________

____

____

Clue: ______________________________

____

4. irregular

Meaning: ______________________________

____

____

Clue: ______________________________

____

F. Reading for Details

Reread the two paragraphs identified below. Then, complete the main idea/detail webs.

Paragraph # 6

Main Idea: ______________________________

____

____

- How recorded?
- When found gone?
- Why gone?

Paragraph # 11

Main Idea: ______________________________

____

____

- How many newly found?
- Which is biggest?
- How big is it?

Neptune

G. Using Words to Know

Some words are missing from the sentences below. Fill in each blank with the correct word from the Words to Know box on the first page of the lesson. Use context clues.

1. Neptune is very far from Earth. Through a telescope, Neptune looks like a blue ____________________ .

2. Neptune moves outside of Pluto for a few years because Pluto has a(n) ____________________ orbit.

3. Uranus appears from Earth to have ____________________ around it. These rings have bright clumps in them.

4. Neptune is almost 3 billion miles from Earth. Even at this distance, people can see this planet from Earth with ____________________ .

H. Making a Diagram

The circle below represents Uranus. Draw a circle to represent the correct size of Neptune.

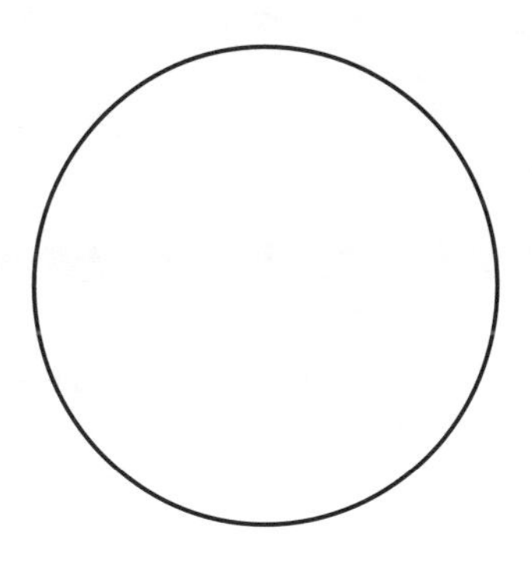

Lesson 14

Pluto

This image shows the planet Pluto (upper left) and its moon, Charon (right).

Pluto

Lesson 14

A. Setting the Stage

Read the first two and last two paragraphs of this lesson. Write four nouns or phrases that appear to be key ideas.

1.	2.	3.	4.

B. Discussing the Background

Reread the last two paragraphs of Lesson 13. As a group, discuss the relationship between Lesson 13 and Lesson 14.

Words to Know
calculate
theory
accurately
ferried

1 Astronomers carefully studied the orbits of Uranus and Neptune. Their orbits were different from what the scientists had **calculated.** When these unusual orbits were first noticed, astronomers began to look for a ninth planet.

2 In 1905, American astronomer Percival Lowell guessed that Uranus and Neptune were being pulled by another planet's gravity. He called this other planet "X." Lowell looked for his Planet X until he died in 1916. He never found it.

3 For the next 14 years, several hard-working astronomers searched for Planet X. In 1930, American astronomer Clyde Tombaugh discovered it with a very powerful telescopic camera. Tombaugh was then working at the Lowell Observatory in Arizona. Tombaugh's pictures clearly showed that a point of light was moving among the stars.

4 The name Pluto was chosen because it is in a very dark, distant place in the solar system. Pluto was the ancient Greek god of the dead and the lower world. He lived in a place that was dark and unfriendly.

5 Pluto is an average distance of 3.67 billion miles from the sun. This makes it the farthest planet from the sun. From Pluto, the sun looks like only a bright star. Pluto's orbit is tilted and very stretched out. This unusual orbit sometimes causes Pluto to swing inside Neptune's orbit. This event took place in 1979. For twenty years, Pluto was closer to the sun than Neptune. On February 11, 1999, Pluto moved beyond Neptune again. Pluto will remain the farthest from the sun until April 5, 2231.

Pluto

Pluto is so far away from Earth that it is the hardest planet to see. Even through the most powerful telescope, it looks like a dim yellow dot of light. No markings on its surface can be seen. **6**

Pluto is far from being a gas giant like Neptune and Uranus. Pluto is actually the smallest planet in the solar system. With a diameter of about 1,430 miles, it is even smaller than Earth's moon. In fact, several other known moons in the solar system are quite a bit larger than Pluto. Pluto's mass is so small that its gravity does not affect the orbits of Uranus or Neptune. Thus, astronomers were not correct in thinking that Pluto was pulling on these two planets. Even though this **theory** was not correct, it helped with the discovery of Pluto. **7**

Because of the theory, scientists spent many hours hunting for a planet. If not for the theory, the hunt probably would not have taken place. Without the careful hunt, far-away Pluto might not have been found. It is likely that the orbits of Uranus and Neptune were not **accurately** measured. New measurements taken by Voyager 2 work in the calculations. **8**

Astronomers think that Pluto is made of frozen gases. They sometimes call it a big orbiting snowball. Pluto probably has a thin nitrogen and methane atmosphere, with a surface made mostly of ice that reflects sunlight brightly. Its surface temperature is close to –400°F (–240°C), making Pluto the coldest planet of all. Inside, Pluto may have a tiny, rocky core that is surrounded by layers of rocks, frozen methane, hydrogen, and water. **9**

Pluto is very slow moving in its long, stretched-out orbit around the sun. A year on Pluto lasts as long as 248 years on Earth. Pluto also spins very slowly on its axis. One complete day on Pluto equals just more than six of Earth's days. **10**

In 1978, American astronomer James W. Christy discovered a large moon orbiting Pluto. He called it Charon, a Greek name for the boatman who **ferried** people across the River Styx into the underworld ruled by Pluto. **11**

For a moon, Charon is very close to Pluto—just more than 12,000 miles away. It orbits Pluto at a speed that matches the speed of the planet. Thus, Charon never sets or rises. Before Charon was discovered, astronomers believed Pluto was a large planet. The images of Charon and Pluto were blurred together. **12**

13

Scientists are still not certain about Pluto's origin. Some continue to wonder if it is a planet at all. Pluto looks more like a moon of the giant planets than a planet itself. Because it has a strange path and is small in size, some astronomers think that it is a very large and far-off asteroid. Still others think it might be a moon that escaped from Neptune's gravitational pull. There are probably more unanswered questions about Pluto than any other planet. Soon, scientists hope to learn more about "Planet X."

14

On December 18, 2004, the Pluto Kuiper Express (PKE) is scheduled to launch. In 2012, PKE is scheduled to reach Pluto. Its mission is to study both Pluto and Charon. Then the craft will continue on to Kuiper belt beyond Pluto. Data will be sent back to Earth.

C. Finding the Main Idea

Highlight or circle the main idea in each paragraph. Remember that the main idea of a paragraph is often the first or last sentence in that paragraph. Other times, the main idea has to be pieced together from more than one sentence.

D. Making a Timeline

Place three important dates from this lesson on the timeline. Write two or three words to identify the importance of each date.

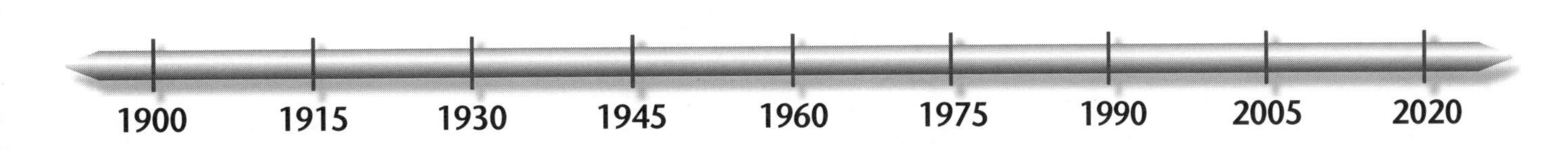

E. Using Words to Know

Some words are missing from the paragraphs below. Fill in each blank with the correct word from the Words to Know box on the first page of the lesson. Use context clues.

1. Astronomers had an idea that Pluto was pulling on Neptune and Uranus. But because Pluto is so small, this ________________ was not correct.

2. Using math, scientists were able to ________________ how Uranus and Neptune should orbit the sun. When the orbits did not match the math figures, a search began for another planet.

3. Pluto's moon is named after the boatman who ________________ people across the River Styx.

4. The search for Pluto was an error. Since some measurements were not ________________ made, scientists were using wrong information. They really had no reason to think another planet existed.

F. Making a Diagram

The circle below represents Pluto. Draw a circle to represent the sun as seen from Pluto.

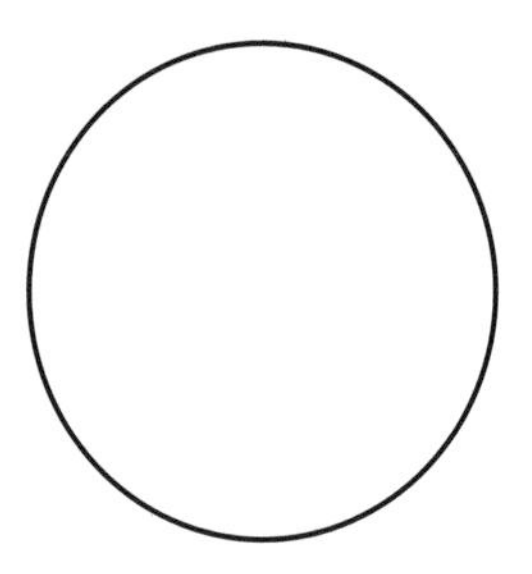

End-of-Book Test

A. Write *True* or *False* for each sentence.

_________ 1. Venus is known as Earth's sister planet.

_________ 2. In some ways, gas planets are like stars.

_________ 3. On Earth, earthquakes happen when crust plates shift.

_________ 4. Ocean tides on Earth are caused by the moon's gravity.

_________ 5. The moons that orbit the planets are mostly smooth, flat bodies of land.

_________ 6. The Milky Way is part of the Solar System.

_________ 7. Neptune is sometimes further from the sun than Pluto.

_________ 8. Stars have a strong force of gravity that can capture other objects.

_________ 9. Like Earth, Mars has several large oceans.

_________ 10. The sun is the largest and most important planet in the solar system.

B. Match each item on the left with the correct detail on the right.

Write each answer on the line.

_____ 1. rilles

_____ 2. polar caps

_____ 3. scarps

_____ 4. planet rings

_____ 5. axis

_____ 6. gullies

_____ 7. heat

_____ 8. PKE

_____ 9. galaxy

_____ 10. supernova

a. both Jupiter and Neptune give off more than they receive

b. spacecraft that will travel to Pluto

c. a star that explodes

d. empty water paths

e. a huge system of stars

f. are made of ice, rock, and dust

g. deep cracks on Earth's moon

h. are a sign of the presence of water on a planet

i. imaginary line on which a planet spins

j. steep, rocky cliffs that zigzag across craters on Mercury

C. Choose the correct answer. Write each answer on the line.

1. A planet ________ in a curved path around the sun.

   a. rotates **b.** tilts **c.** spins **d.** revolves

2. In 1986, Voyager 2 flew past Uranus and it found ________ .

   a. 10 new moons **b.** running water **c.** living plants **d.** nothing new

3. The chromosphere is a layer of ________ 's atmosphere.

   a. Venus **b.** Earth **c.** the moon **d.** the sun

4. Earth's craters are believed to have been caused by ________ that crashed into the planet.

   a. moons **b.** comets **c.** meteorites **d.** satellites

5. Io and ________ are two of Jupiter's moons.

   a. Europa **b.** Pluto **c.** Cassini **d.** Voyager

6. The Milky Way is a ________ .

   a. satellite **b.** galaxy **c.** universe **d.** comet

7. The moon is a ________ of the Earth.

   a. satellite **b.** sister planet **c.** volcano **d.** star

8. The planet farthest from the sun is ________.

   a. Mercury **b.** Jupiter **c.** Pluto **d.** Mars

9. The Earth needs about ________ to travel around the sun once.

   a. 24 hours **b.** 7 days **c.** 30 days **d.** 365 days

10. ________ was the first person to walk on the moon.

    a. Neil Armstrong **b.** Edwin Hubble **c.** Galileo Galilei **d.** Percival Lowell

D. Circle the word or phrase that correctly completes each sentence.

1. (Saturn, Earth, Mercury) is 93 million miles from the sun.
2. The axis of (Uranus, Earth, Mars) is so tilted that the planet looks like it is on its side.
3. (Mars, Mercury, Jupiter) is one of Earth's two neighbors.
4. The closest planet to the sun is (Mercury, Mars, Earth).
5. (Pluto, Earth, Jupiter) is the largest planet.

E. Answer the following questions with complete sentences.

1. Why would life on Earth not exist without the sun?

____

____

____

____

2. How are the length of a planet's year and day determined?

____

____

____

____

GLOSSARY

A

accurately—exactly or correctly (88)

alignment—arrangement in a straight line (40)

alter—to change (28)

ancient—very old (57)

arcs— curved lines (82)

asteroid—piece of rock in space that orbits the sun (10)

astronaut—member of the crew of a spacecraft (33)

astronomer—one who studies the planets and stars (11)

astronomy—study of the planets and stars (75)

axis—imaginary line around which a planet turns (9)

B

binoculars—device designed for use with both eyes that makes distant objects seem larger (81)

black dwarf—final stage of a star's life (15)

C

calculate—to find out by using math; to compute (87)

canyon—a narrow valley with steep walls (58)

captured asteroid—(71)

carbon dioxide—a colorless, odorless gas (46)

channel—a stream or river bed (58)

chromosphere—lower part of the sun's atmosphere (22)

clash—two unlike things coming together (34)

comet—wide body of ice, metal, gas, and dust that orbits the sun (10)

confirm—to make sure something is correct; to prove(64)

constellation—group of stars in a recognized pattern (16)

continent—one of seven large land masses on the earth (52)

core—the central or inside of an object (22)

corona—the outer, hottest part of the sun's atmosphere (23)

crater—a round hole or impression on a planet or moon's surface

crust—the solid outer part of the earth (52)

D

data—information, often represent by numbers (34)

debris—pieces or fragments scattered about (65)

dense—thick (69)

detect—to find, discover, or notice (64)

diameter—distance through the center of a circle or sphere (76)

disk—a flat, round, thin object; a flat surface of the sun, a moon, or a planet (81)

E

emit—to give off (22)

enormous—very large (70)

erupt—to explode to burst forth (64)

evolve—to change gradually over time (27)

F

ferried—carried across a river or lake (88)

fluke—a chance happening that is not planned (27)

G

galaxy—group of billions of stars (11)

giant planets—planets that consist mostly of gases (63)

glacier—a large mass of ice moving over land (77)

gravity—force that pulls objects to the center of the earth or other body in space (15)

greenhouse effect—warming caused by gasses in the atmosphere trapping heat from the ground (46)

gullies—narrow ditches or water paths (76)

H

haze—smoke or dust in the air (46)

hollow—having nothing inside (69)

I

insulator—something that does not allow heat or energy to pass through (45)

interstellar—between the stars (28)

irregular—not following the normal pattern (83)

J

jagged—having rough edges (77)

L

lava—hot, liquid rock that flows from a volcano (40)

light-year—distance that light travels in one year (16)

lunar—relating to the moon (34)

M

magnetic field—space around an object in which an attractive force occurs (53)

mantle—layer of the earth under the crust and above the core (52)

mass—a very large object or area (21); amount of matter an object takes up (51)

matter—material things are made of (9)

meteor—piece of rock or metal traveling though space that enters Earth's atmosphere (10)

meteorite—piece of rock or metal that has fallen from space to a planet or moon (10)

meteoroid—piece of rock or metal traveling through space (10)

microscopic—too small to be seen with the naked eye (69)

molten—melted (52)

N

nebula—cloud of dust and gas from which stars are formed (16)

nova—star that suddenly becomes very bright, then fades to its original brightness (16)

O

observatory—building that has telescopes and other instruments for viewing objects in outer space (76)

particle—very small piece (22)

phase—the shape of the visible part of the moon at a given time (33)

photosphere—surface of the sun (22)

plain—a flat area of land (34)

polar caps—areas of ice at the North and South Poles of the earth (57)

probe—spacecraft that measures and reports information (58)

R

GLOSSARY

radar—system to find unseen objects by reflecting sound waves (40)

revolve—to move in a curved path around a central object (9)

rilles—(34)

rings—thin circles of dust, ice, and other material surrounding a planet (69)

rotation—act of turning around a center line or axis (52)

S

satellite—object in outer space that revolves around a planet or moon (10)

scarp—steep, rocky cliff following a jagged line (40)

solar flare—a sudden eruption on the surface of the sun (22)

spiral—a winding, circular coil that gradually gets bigger (28)

stable—not moving or changing; steady (45)**star cluster**—group of stars that appear to be close to each other in the sky (16)

sulfur crystals—particles of sulfur, a light yellow element that burns easily (45)

sulfuric acid—heavy, colorless, destructive acid (46)

supernova—star that explodes, becoming extremely bright, brighter than a nova (16)

T

telescope—instrument that makes far away objects appear closer and larger (16)

terrain—area of land and its features (34)

terrestrial—having to do with land or solid matter (9)

theory—idea that needs to be proved (88)

tilt—to tip or slant at an angle(75)

trace—a small amount (46)

tremor—a shaking or vibrating movement (52)

twilight—time just after sunset when there is still light in the sky (39)

U

ultraviolet—related to invisible rays of light (58)

unaided—without help (39)

universe—the expanse of space in which stars and planets are located (16)

V

volcano—opening on the surface of a planet through which dust, steam, and lava erupt (34)

W

water vapor—water in a gaseous state